Might Make You Smile

Brenda Burling

First Published 2017 by:
Matthew James Publishing Ltd
Unit 46 Goyt Mill
Upper Hibbert Lane
Marple
SK6 7HX
www.matthewjamespublishing.com

ISBN: 978-1-910265-37-6

Printed by Gutenberg

Illustrations by Angela Chick
www.angelachick.com

This book has been written for, and is dedicated to, all those affected by cancer, past, present, and future.

Humour can be a weapon against disease; shared humour is twice as strong.

B.B.

Contents

Nerf Attack | *Susan*   11

Ball Bearing Bracelet | *Kay*   16

Hair Today, Gone Tonight | *June*   18

A Night Out With Kylie | *Clare*   21

Mr & Mrs Salt
and Pepper Pot | *Anon*   23

Not My Finest Hour | *Jo*   26

Pammies | *Anon*   30

White Van Man | *Sadie*   34

Green with
Envy, not so much | *Michelle*   38

Take Aim, Fire! | *Jan J*   42

Help, Shark! | *Anon*   45

Sherry Love, Sherry. | *Anita*   49

Drip, Drip, Drip. | *Anon*   55

Marks Out Of Ten | *Susan & Casey*   60

Is it a Bird?
Is it a Plane? | *Inspired by Michelle*   66

Catch That! | *Margaret*   72

Groundhog Day Radio | *Jan*   79

Back to front,
Top to Bottom | *Ffion*   82

Double Up Dolly | *Inspired by Anita*   85

Hair There, Really? | *Anon*   89

Knitting, Not Such
An Innocent Hobby | *Margaret*   92

Bowel Class
not Bowls Class | *Julie*   94

The Swimming
Hat Brigade | *Anon*   98

H.H.C. (Happy
Herceptin Cattle) | *Anita C* 101

Lucky Black Cats? | *Jan J* 104

Chick, Chick Hair | *Clare* 107

New Hairdo
Grandma? | *Polly* 109

Is That You Dad?
Or Is That Me? | *Clare* 111

Running Away With You | *Sadie* 113

Oooh! I Love Your Hairdo | *Anon* 117

Drop Dead Gorgeous | *Michelle* 120

Not Exactly Nicky Clarke | *Myer* 123

Treatment
Tag Team | *Lesley, Lynn & Don* 125

On The Run | *Clare* 131

Love You Mum | *Sadie* 134

And The Award Goes To | *Anon* 136

A Bit Like
Grooming The Dog | *Susan*   141

Olympic Hopes? | *Anon*   144

Questioning
Professor Hawking | *Del & Peter*   147

May The Force
Be With You | *Tana*   150

For The Camera | *Irene*   153

I'm Forever
Blowing Bubbles | *Val*   155

Wind, What wind? | *Michelle*   159

White As A Ghost | *Elsie and Cathleen*   161

Opposite Ends | *Myer*   164

Hello Little Old Lady | *Margaret*   166

Lizzie's Denial | *Anon*   168

How's Your Ears? | *Michelle*   171

Susan

Nerf Attack

Susan was a thirty-something-year-old mum of two lively boys. Having been diagnosed with Breast Cancer, she had undergone all the treatments and was looking forward to getting her life back on track. With her family by her side, and her faith she knew she could withstand anything. Her cancer had taught her so many lessons. She felt she had found her 'real' friends, and was surprised that sometimes those she had thought were closest, had not always proven to be so. But Susan had also learnt that there was no right or wrong way to deal with the 'C' word and that everyone was entitled to their own approach.

She felt that she had gone through hell and back, as had her family, but now she wanted to focus on being 'normal' again. Her appearance wasn't by any means all-consuming, but she was the first to admit that her goal of feeling as much like her old self as possible did, to a degree, include how she looked.

There came the day when she was having the final touches to her breast reconstruction, and it was the time she had been truly looking forward to, she liked to call it "nipple time". Having had the breast reconstruction done in stages, this was literally the 'cherry on the cake'. Nipples were to be created and added to her already reconstructed, and much loved 'boobs'.

The morning came and the operation went off without a hitch. The specialist surgeon created the nipples and had attached them with infinite care and precision. Bound and dressed, Susan was glad to be going home to heal. This, to her, was the final stages of completing and surviving her cancer; and ultimately thriving as a woman, wife, and mother. She couldn't wait to see the end results. The surgeon had warned her that the dressings would be there for a time, it was vital she took things very slowly, and she adheres to her surgeon's words on how to help aid in her recovery. Susan couldn't wait for the day she could remove the dressings, she knew she would enjoy the great unveiling.

Life carried on with a home and family to look after. Susan was careful to keep her exertion to a minimum, and the whole family made fun of her for resembling a mummy with her dressings.

Susan waited patiently for the day when she could remove the final dressing. Being the mother of lively boys, she had learnt to dodge most missiles, glide over Lego, always be up for sporting licky, sticky tattoos to be stuck in various inappropriate places, and deal with pretty much everything her offspring had launched her way.

Getting dressed one morning she was a little slower than normal, and was momentarily taken by surprise by her youngest, liveliest son, who was currently in the guise of an elite assassin. Armed with a Nerf gun fully loaded with its foam-tipped bullets and safety catch off, she heard the sharp click and felt the ping before she could remove herself from its line of fire. Zap! The bullet had hit its intended target spot on. Mum had been got. The tiny assassin fled the scene of the crime with a drop and roll maneuver that James Bond would have been proud of, his mission had been accomplished.

What had actually been shot at, with perfect aim and precision, was one of her brand new, still settling themselves in, and already much loved nipples. As Susan looked downwards she already knew all was not well. She called for her husband – who as luck would have it was a paramedic – not long recovered from a long night shift, but fortunately home that day. He quickly came to the bedroom to find his wife attempting to reposition the much longed for nipple.

Her husband, being the more medically minded of the couple, knew what he had to do. Susan insisted she didn't want to go back to the specialist, stating that after such a long time with treatment upon treatment you only went to the hospital when you absolutely had to. Between Susan and her husband, they lovingly and ever so carefully repositioned the nipple and he steri-stripped that little bud right back into place as best he could. Disaster, they hoped, had been diverted.

A while later, back at the hospital for the follow-up appointment with the surgeon who had performed Susan's procedure, Susan removed her top. She stood absolutely still, staring frontwards, hardly able to breathe. There followed a great deal of frowning and quizzical examinations of her breasts. Susan and her husband avoided eye contact with each other and the consultant. Susan held her breath for what seemed like an age. The surgeon finally gave his verdict; he wasn't happy with the alignment of the nipples and felt at least one should be redone. He did question how one nipple seemed somewhat misplaced and couldn't quite understand how it had come about.

Susan countered that she was in fact delighted with the results, and there was really no need to spend any more time on her breasts. After all, she was happy, healthy, and getting on with life; that was what mattered. Susan also pointed out that nobody had perfect breasts anyway; a little uniqueness added to the authenticity, and she shared a knowing smile with her husband. They then left the hospital for the last time.

Kay
Ball Bearing Bracelet

Kay loved her bracelets. There were three of them made of silver, and they held charms that she had collected which signified the momentous events of her life: from having children, wedding anniversaries, and everything in-between. She wore the bracelets often and loved all that they represented.

Kay was well-known as the sort of person who could make a dull day bright. She had an uncanny knack for cheering up those around her, and possessed a wicked sense of fun and humour. It was Kay people went to when they were down; her positivity shone through, and you couldn't help but smile when you met her. She worked in an old-people's home and loved her job. The residents adored her creativity, and nothing was ever too much trouble for her.

As she was undergoing tests and scans for her diagnosed breast cancer, she had to have ball bearings placed on her breasts for one particular procedure, a guided wire mammogram. She smiled to herself as she had an idea. The procedures seemed to take forever, but when they were finally over she pulled the consultant to one side. At first he thought he had misheard and asked Kay to repeat herself. She slowly and deliberately stated her request once more. The consultant was a little taken aback, but then smiled and said he would have to speak to various people; he would get back to her.

During her next appointment, Kay left the consultant's office smiling to herself. The ball bearings that had been used in the scan, now have pride of place on bracelet number three. Kay loves to show off her bracelet and watch people's reactions when she explains the significance of the ball bearings. She has survived breast cancer, and she loves to look at the ball bearings as a reminder of what she has gone through and how she loves her life. They now share a place alongside all the other great and important events of her life. Kay also loves the shock value of them; they never fail to make people smile.

June
Hair Today, Gone Tonight

June may have been in her seventies, but she still loved to go out, socialise, and enjoy herself. Her cancer treatments often meant that she wasn't always able to do the things she loved to do; she was not always feeling well enough. When the good days came, and June could go out with her friends and partner, she loved nothing more than going out for a drink or to dinner for the evening.

It was a "good" day, and June was looking forward to going out that night with her partner. The cancer treatments had meant that June had lost her hair, but she had decided she would wear a wig that night. She didn't often wear one, feeling more comfortable without, but she felt she would make the effort that evening. She was pleased with the result in the mirror and was looking forward to an evening of fun. Her new glossy hair swished around her shoulders, and the fringe gave her a whole new glamorous look. June was feeling like a million dollars.

June, her partner, and friends had chosen a lively pub for the evening. She was soaking up the atmosphere; everyone seemed to be on good form, and she was enjoying herself. After a couple of drinks, a friend leant towards June, being deaf, June read her lips. She could see that her friend was suggesting she go to the ladies. Somewhat puzzled, June followed her friend to the toilets.

Pushing open the heavy door, June gasped as she saw her reflection in the mirror. The wig had slid completely to one side, and the fringe was by her chin. One minute June was laughing at the ridiculousness of her reflection, the next she was cross that none of her party had mentioned anything sooner. The more she looked at her reflection the more she laughed, she decided she looked more like an obscure version of 'Cousin Itt' from the Addams Family than anything else. She straightened her wig and returned to the bar, but it was at that point June decided wigs were not for her. Although she kept the wig on until the end of the evening she acknowledged she felt much more 'herself' once the hairpiece was tucked away in her bag at the end of the night.

As much as June enjoyed the glamour of the wig, she wasn't sure if she enjoyed the laughter her 'Cousin Itt' impersonation brought her and her friends more.

June has never worn a wig again and she still berates her friends for not informing her sooner of her 'wardrobe malfunction'. Even now, she cannot finish telling the story without bursting out laughing thinking of the absurdity of her reflection in the mirror that night. Proving wigs are not for all, and certainly not for June.

Clare
A Night Out With Kylie

Kylie was the name given to Clare's newly acquired, highly fashionable, and fabulously glossy wig. Even though Clare came from a family of fashion and beauty conscious hairdressing females, she had adapted to her hair loss during her cancer treatment pretty quickly. She had, in fact, found it character building. In the grand scheme of things a little hair loss was not something she concerned herself with.

However, Clare did, on occasion, take Kylie out. With a night out coming up, Clare decided she would wear Kylie. With a final check of her appearance and with Kylie firmly in place, Clare was ready for some fun.

A great night of chatting, eating, drinking, and plenty of laughter was exactly what Clare enjoyed. Soon it was time to leave, and everyone was saying their goodbyes. Clare went round the group hugging everyone, In mid-hug with one particular friend Clare felt an odd sensation; Kylie was on the move! Unfortunately, the beautiful bracelet worn by her friend had become caught in Kylie, and the much-admired wig was slowly making its way off Clare's head and heading toward her shoulders. The bracelet wearing friend was mortified; the restaurant was full and the incident was sure to have been noticed by the other diners. Clare couldn't help but laugh as Kylie and the bracelet were separated. It took all of her reassurances, between fits of giggles, to mollify her friend, then her friend finally began to see the funny side. Clare joked that Kylie had always had the capability to draw plenty of attention.

Anon

Mr & Mrs Salt and Pepper Pot

When Mrs Salt was diagnosed with cancer and lost her hair very quickly due to her chemotherapy, it was initially distressing for her, but she came to terms with it and life carried on, as it so often does. It was only when Mr and Mrs Salt's children were getting confused by their parents' appearance from the back, that the Salt's came up with an ingenious plan. Mrs Salt didn't like the feel of a hairpiece or wig, they made her hot and uncomfortable, she was never able to keep it on straight, and it felt like she was wearing a hat all the time – which wasn't particularly her style either. As busy as she was at home, she felt they just seemed to get in her way, so she decided to wear nothing.

Mr Salt had been bald all his adult life and that was no big deal until Mrs Salt's diagnosis and subsequent treatment. From the back, the little Salt's were becoming confused, they couldn't always tell their parents apart; often thinking they were calling out to dad when in fact they were talking to mum and vice-versa. The frustrations of the Salt family were heightened when the children would demand school uniforms and packed lunches from a fearful looking Mr Salt; who didn't know where to start looking for such mysterious items. would panic, and run to find Mrs Salt.

Mr and Mrs Salt were at home together one day while the little Salts were at school, and they came up with a marvellous plan. Mrs Salt found a thick eyeshadow pencil in a chocolate brown shade. Mr Salt wrote on the back of Mrs Salt's head 'MUM' in neat, large letters. In turn, Mrs Salt wrote on the back of Mr Salt's head 'DAD'. The little Salts came home from school that day and were delighted with their parent's efforts; harmony was restored in the Salt household.

The Salts were able to adapt their heads for an upcoming Fancy Dress Party by simply adding one single circle in the centre of Mrs Salt's head, and three circles on Mr Salt's head. Mr and Mrs Salt went to the Fancy Dress as salt and pepper pots. Not only did they delight their children with their creativity, they won first prize at the Fancy Dress Party.

Jo
Not My
Finest Hour

Jo had always been someone who you could have written a thousand amusing stories about her. An intelligent woman who had a flare for art and design and loved dogs, cats, and every other animal you could imagine. Jo was a woman to whom a lot of things happened to. She had some amazing stories about events that were almost too incredible to believe, but you knew they were actually true. If there were ever to be a stampeding herd of wildebeest rampaging through the countryside, the spectacle would have happened in Jo's neck of the woods; and it would have been nothing unusual if they had targeted Jo's beautiful garden to charge through. There had been lost dogs, chickens, even donkeys, wandering the country lanes and it was to Jo's house they headed for. Her friends loved her dearly anyway, but all the more for her regaling of an average day in her life.

Jo was diagnosed with cancer in December, and after numerous consultations and surgeries, her radiotherapy treatment was to begin in March. Prior to the treatment there were various scans and tests to be carried out. Jo had been given an appointment for an early morning scan and had set her alarm clock accordingly to allow for plenty of time to get to the hospital.

The day did not start well. The alarm did not go off and Jo, who had been unable to sleep properly for weeks (another symptom of her cancer), had slept soundly all night. When she finally woke, she knew instinctively she was late. As luck would have it, she also acknowledged she was having a 'bad' day because her energy levels were already low. Added to this, was her ability to only locate antique knickers of an undecipherable shade and no bra – it had inexplicably disappeared in the space of twelve hours. She suspected one of the family dogs but had no time or energy to track down the culprit. She quickly resigned herself to having to go out with only fifty percent of her underwear, reasoning she would have probably had to remove the item anyway for the scan. On time, notwithstanding a household search, she left for the hospital only to hit rush hour traffic almost immediately.

Sitting in traffic, Jo seized the opportunity. She delved quickly into her bag in an attempt to at least locate a hairbrush to try and tame her wayward head of thick, curly hair which had amassed itself into an impressive "bed-head" beehive hairdo. It was then that she realised she had in fact picked up the wrong bag and was minus any cosmetics or grooming paraphernalia. Jo scooped out the crumby contents of the bag onto the passenger seat, only to find a couple of hairy, slightly gooey Haribo sweets, and a long forgotten, possibly unpaid, parking ticket.

Eventually arriving at the hospital, she was shown into her cubicle and given a gown to wear during her scan. Cursing the bralessness of her upper body, the skimpiness of the gown, and its inability to barely meet where it should, but congratulating herself on guessing correctly that she would be asked to remove the garment anyway. She cursed to herself once more about the shapelessness and dubious shade of her knickers, only adding to her less than glamorous appearance when she bolted upright, startled by a knock on her cubicle door. The surprise of the knock found her banging her head with some force on the shoe shelf above, and then stubbing her toe while in the process of trying to open the cubicle door. Unable to stop the torrent of colourful expletives blurting from her mouth, in walks "Dr Drop-Dead Gorgeous." A man at least ten years her junior, broad-shoul-dered, and looking like he stepped off the set of E.R. or Grey's Anatomy. As well as greeting her doctor red-faced, foul-mouthed, bare-chested, and rubbing her head, Jo also happened to notice that the large clock on the wall behind him was showing it was ten-thirty. The day had hardly begun.

Anon

Pammies

Being in her sixties, Ina found that fashion had skipped past her. She was happy to pick up on perhaps the odd one or two styles, but no longer had the desperate need to be completely up to date with her wardrobe. She was now happy to be comfortable above all else.

She liked to think she watched her weight and was careful in the amount of wine she consumed; she liked to think that, but reality didn't always match up. Nevertheless, she was a lady who knew life was for living, and that a little overindulgence every now and then was good for the soul.

The tiniest pinprick of blood on the inside of her bra cup was the only indication Ina had that there was the very faint possibility that something wasn't quite right. Thanks to quick action on her and her doctor's part, produced the positive test results revealed during a follow-up appointment that Ina had breast cancer. Although shocked and a little scared, Ina was a woman of common sense and cast iron will; she was prepared for the treatments that would come next.

After a double mastectomy and chemotherapy, she already considered herself to be on the home stretch of her 'run-in' with cancer, which was how she preferred to think of her illness; a blip that life throws you from time-to-time. It was only when the reconstruction surgery was discussed and finally scheduled that she gave any thought to her appearance. Ina was surprised at how her opinion of herself had subtly changed.

Suddenly she was shopping for summer clothes; off the shoulder dresses and strappy sun tops. Ina had a vision of something in her mind that she had never considered before. She knew there was one thing she now craved more than anything, a red one-piece swimming costume. Ina kept her longing a secret. She planned a grand unveiling, poolside, on the next family holiday.

Finding a one-piece in bright red took almost as long as the completion of the reconstruction surgery itself. On a cold March morning while browsing in a department store, she came across the longed for item. Finding a size to fit had been a minor issue. The assistant rang the supplier who confirmed that although there was not a demand for that particular size, they did stock them, and one would be sent over with the next delivery.

Ina recovered from all the surgery and treatments; she had lost a little weight but not so much to make a difference in her wardrobe. The day Ina's consultant gave her the great news that she was well again, was only a couple of months before the family holiday. Ina's excitement grew with every passing day running up to her longed for holiday.

The sun beat down intensely as Ina and three generations of her family touched down in Spain. The villa was perfect, with a huge pool, enormous gardens and terraces, and enough room for all of the grandchildren to run around and have a great time. With bags unpacked and swimming costumes on, everyone made their way down to the pool. Ina kept her sarong tied in the style of a dress so as to not spoil her unveiling. When everyone was in the pool Ina untied her sarong. The grandchildren cheered and clapped, Ina's children who were grown up and with children of their own, bobbed around open mouthed staring at their mother in shock, and then they too whooped and clapped.

"If Nannie's got to have pammies, then she'll have the swimming costume to match." Ina laughed as she struck a slow-motion running pose, just like Pamela Anderson in Baywatch. The red swimming costume, and Ina's new figure, was laughed and talked about all holiday by the whole family. From that moment on Ina's breasts were known to all as her 'pammies', and the red swimming costume became a family legend.

Sadie
White Van Man

Sadie had tried to keep her hair as straight and neat as possible, but the warm summer weather was making it difficult. Keeping the beautifully cut and styled ash blonde wig straight and in place was not easy.

It was a hot summer's day, and although the studio was air-conditioned, the amount of equipment used to keep the radio station going meant there was still heat emitting around her desk. The drugs she was taking as part of her cancer treatment also meant her internal 'temperature gauge', as she liked to call it, was often on the blink. Sometimes she fluctuated from being excessively hot and then very cold, usually at inappropriate times.

On this particular day, she could already feel her head was molten beneath the mesh of the hairpiece. Her fingers felt under the hair and touched the soft fuzziness of her own regrowth. Sadie knew it would be a few more months before her own hair would be noticeable again, and she often wondered what colour it would come back as. With the heat beneath the wig intensifying and making her uncomfortable, Sadie counted down the ten minutes left of the radio show and longed for the time when she could make her way home and walk in the fresh air.

She finished up with a good laugh with a listener who had called in to tell the story of how his cat had run around with a small bird in its mouth for half an hour while being madly chased by the owner. Upon capture, the owner found that what he thought to be a fowl was, in fact, the remnants of his dinner of sausages, pinched from his plate while he had gone to answer the telephone.

Leaving the radio station, Sadie stepped out into the sunshine. The crossing outside the studio was busy; lunchtime meant an increase in the traffic, and there was a crossroad junction immediately off a large roundabout. Sadie's head was really beginning to itch and feel doubly uncomfortable, stepping out onto the crossing she couldn't bear it any longer. In a single movement, she grabbed the wig and plucked it from her head. Then followed a series of unexpected events.

The sound of car horns used in anger and the screeching of brakes filled the air. Sadie turned, enjoying the deliciousness of the cool air against her scalp and was smiling as she turned. It was then that she saw the large white van, which had stopped abruptly at the crossing. Its passengers, she guessed, were builders judging by the writing emblazoned on all the surfaces of the van. She registered three expressions of absolute shock; mouths wide open, eyes bulging, and looking directly at her. She could also hear a strange sound, it was the yell of disbelief emanating from each of the open mouths, "Whoa Mrs!". It took a moment for Sadie to realise that the rest of the traffic commotion was due to the van straddling two lanes. Its occupants had obviously stopped the van sharply having seen a blonde haired lady effectively scalp herself in broad daylight.

Sadie was unable to help herself; she was laughing as she apologised profusely to the van's clearly traumatised occupants and the other traffic that had been forced to stop suddenly. She explained she was absolutely fine and that there was nothing to worry about; trying desperately not to laugh at the burly men who were still clearly shocked by what they had seen. Enjoying the coolness of the summer air, Sadie made her way home laughing loudly to herself every time she pictured the three faces in the white van.

Michelle
Green with Envy, not so much…

Michelle was late for work. It didn't seem to matter how much earlier she set the alarm, time appeared to elude her. She could have blamed it on the effects of the chemotherapy treatment for her ovarian cancer, but she never did. Sometimes she just didn't feel like herself, but she managed to shake that feeling by the time she got to the office.

Working was not for everyone who was experiencing life with cancer, but for Michelle it was important on many levels. It was something she had always done – been a hard worker – so when she became ill she tried her best to fit in work around it and the subsequent treatments. Unfortunately, the cancer returned on an almost annual basis and each time Michelle dealt with it with a renewed stoicism. She often liked to joke that her husband had a new woman every year for probably the last five years. The chemotherapy treatment had meant the loss of her hair, but each time it had grown back it had come through a different colour and texture, it had been straight, curly, thick, and thin.

Michelle had found wearing a wig something that had become a bit of a routine; as had remembering to pencil on eyebrows every morning. She often felt it was the eyebrows more than anything that completed and framed a face, giving it definition. Afterall, with so many different hairstyles and accessories that could cover a head, hair sometimes went almost unseen. Hats, scarves, and headbands all aided in covering or filling in what was actually on top of your head, but eyebrows are just there on the front of the face and taken for granted, but definitely missed when they are gone.

Michelle looked at the clock once more, again it had lurched forward dramatically, and she was definitely on the late side now. Quickly, she pencilled on the well-practiced arch over each eye. Grabbing her shoes, and her favourite bag, she made a dash for the front door.

The railway station was abuzz with the low rumble of commuters; who were waiting to be crammed like sardines on the train to Liverpool Street Station. There were many familiar faces, and all were smiling in Michelle's direction as she boarded the train. She was fortunate enough to get a seat sitting opposite a middle aged man reading the daily newspaper. He acknowledged her with a nod and, with what Michelle thought was a quizzical look. She wondered if he thought he recognised her from somewhere, but he certainly didn't seem familiar to her.

The train finally pulled into Liverpool Street Station. Michelle could feel her mouth becoming dry, as often happened; another side effect of the drugs used in her treatment. She needed to buy some water and a packet of chewing gum, she knew this would help alleviate the problem, so she headed for the nearest newsagent. Standing in line waiting to pay, Michelle was becoming increasingly aware of people's stares. Strangers were looking in her direction, their gazes lingering just a fraction too long. She was beginning to feel a little self-conscious and checked her outfit. She was wearing a smart business suit, check; no holes in tights, check; matching shoes, check; nothing seemed out of place.

As soon as she reached her office building, she headed straight to the ladies toilets. Under the harsh, bright lights, it became gloriously obvious to her why her appearance had caused so much interest. As expertly as her eyebrows were drawn on, there was one small detail she hadn't noticed while hurriedly doing her make-up that morning. The pencil she had used was not her usual soft brown shade. No, today she was sporting what could only be described as an almost metallic emerald shade, with plenty of sparkle. It was fair to say she would not have looked out of place as an extra on any science-fiction blockbuster film set. Laughing at her reflection, she promised herself she would pay more attention when applying her make-up, especially in the gloom of early mornings.

10

Jan J
Take Aim, Fire!

Jan thought she had got away with most of the possible, even predictable, side effects that her cancer treatment could bestow. That was until she was hit by unrelenting nausea, the inability to keep anything down, even water, and the feeling of absolute exhaustion. She tried desperately to put on a brave face, but it was becoming increasingly obvious that she was on the verge of dehydration and that her strength had been severely affected by the inability to eat anything.

Jan resigned herself to the fact that she would need to be admitted to hospital. It was a tough decision to make but it was one Jan had always known could happen. She hated more than anything leaving her family, but it was their insistence that she get some medication, rest, and sustenance, that made her brave enough to make the call.

Jan put on a good show of being upbeat and positive about going into hospital, she didn't want to worry the loved ones around her, but she admitted to herself she was feeling terrible. Once tucked up in bed, in what was lovingly referred to as The Penthouse Suite – actually being the top floor of Addenbrook's Hospital – and settled in with I.V.s for hydration and drugs to help with her symptoms, she was finally able to get some rest. The nausea however was unrelenting, and she was truly grateful when sleep finally came.

Jan woke to the sound of some sort of alarm. Panicking, she checked her pumps and I.V. lines, but everything looked fine, and the noise didn't seem to be coming from any of her equipment. It was at that exact moment that she realised the sound was the buzzer announcing visiting time, simultaneously she experienced a powerful wave of nausea that completely engulfed her. She was powerless, and as if in slow motion she projectile vomited. She watched in horror as the contents of her stomach arched midair, and landed almost perfectly into her open handbag situated at the end of her bed.

At that very same moment, Jan could hear with crystal clarity, "Nice shot mum!" It was

the unmistakable voice of her son, the whole
family had come to visit her. It was unanimously
agreed that Jan could not have performed the
feat again if she tried. Jan bade a fond farewell
to her handbag, there was to be no resurrection
for it from that onslaught. Ironically, that was
the last time Jan was sick; it was agreed it was
a grand finale for sure.

Anon

Help, Shark!

Vera was a proud grandmother, and loved to fill her time with doing as much as possible with her grandchildren. Even before she received the diagnosis of breast cancer, she would take them swimming at the local swimming pool every Sunday and then they would all return home to enjoy Sunday lunch together.

Vera had known in her heart that something wasn't quite right; she hadn't been feeling one hundred percent. Then she discovered a small lump, no bigger than a pea, in her left breast. A short time after, she had been diagnosed with breast cancer. The biggest blow to come to terms with initially was the lack of energy she had, and the fact that she missed out on the time spent with her grandchildren.

Vera's treatment went on longer than she had expected and her recovery hit a few bumps in the road, but slowly she began to feel stronger. The surgery to remove both breasts had been hard to come to terms with and she felt she wanted to pause before considering any further reconstructive surgery. She opted for prosthetic breast implants that were worn inside custom made underwear and even swimwear. Vera eventually got the hang of wearing her 'additions' and although not ideal, they did give her the confidence to do the everyday things she had always loved to do.

After a time, Vera felt confident enough to start taking her grandchildren swimming again at the local pool and this boosted her confidence even more. She was feeling stronger every day and made the decision that a family holiday was called for. She had been swimming a few times with the family and was now at ease with her appearance, and she needed to feel the sun on her skin and sand between her toes.

It was settled, and a family holiday in the sun was agreed upon and booked. Vera made sure she packed extra 'chicken fillets', as the prosthetics were now called by her and her friends at the breast clinic. She wanted to be able to change outfits relatively quickly and it was easier if the 'fillets' were already in place in a few garments. The holiday departure date came around quickly and the family was excited by everything, from the airport to reaching their hotel. Almost a whole week had passed and the family was happy and relaxed. Everyone had a lovely tan and had enjoyed every minute exploring new beaches and restaurants.

One morning during the second week, Vera was taking the grandchildren swimming at the local beach. The sun was shining but there was a little breeze, and the water wasn't quite as calm as it had been; it was now cresting in small waves. The children bounded around regardless, dipping in and out of the surf, pretending to be dolphins and sharks. They loved the added excitement of the waves and, being strong swimmers, Vera was happy to keep an eye on them while enjoying the waves picking her up and carrying her to the shore.

As she was swimming out to slightly deeper water, she noticed something glinting in the sunlight. There were a few people near her, and the children made their way out towards where she was treading water. Vera realised in a moment what the object was and knew she had to take drastic action. "Shark", she yelled at the top of her voice. Everyone looked momentarily in her direction and then headed quickly for the shore, shrieks of 'shark, shark' filling the air. The children were already squealing and making their way back in the direction they had just come from. In one quick movement Vera had grabbed the object and squeezed it back into the cup of her bathing suit.

She then quickly swam back to the shore laughing and apologising loudly to everyone on the beach for scaring them. Everyone's expressions changed, and soon all were laughing at the 'crazy English lady'. Vera apologised to her grandchildren who told her off with plenty of 'Oh, Gran, only you could think you had seen a shark!' Vera laughed off the teasing while discreetly adjusting her swimming costume.

On the way back to the hotel where the family were staying Vera found a supermarket; it had a stationery section and she found some superglue. When everyone was back in their rooms getting ready for dinner, Vera sat crossed legged in her bedroom glueing 'chicken fillets' into each of her bathing suits. She had no intentions of letting another 'shark' spoil her holiday.

Anita

Sherry Love, Sherry.

Anita was the sort of woman who came up with an idea and ran with it. Whatever it took, as long as she truly believed in whatever it was, she had the sort of personality that wouldn't allow her to leave something on her mind alone. Some, usually those close to her, may have even described her as obsessive. However, any label given to Anita never bothered her a bit. She knew where she was heading, at least the desired end result anyway. How she got there was left to fate, destiny, and her own dogged determination to make things happen.

Working with people was her biggest passion. She chaired business networking groups, set up charity events (even in her own back garden), and had created a new cancer support group with a co-founder that had run another group previously. Anita secured a beautiful venue to hold the once-a-month meetings, a country hotel and golf club. Once the word had been put out, the response was fantastic; Anita was thrilled with the feedback from those who attended. The feeling of togetherness, empathy, and moral support oozed from the light and airy hotel drawing room where the group met.

Anita worked hard to make sure she had guest speakers, healthcare advisors, and various treatment providers on hand. The time flew by, and the group went from strength to strength. With great publicity, and an excellent reputation as a sanctuary for cancer sufferers, in no time the group was promoted in every hospital and doctor's waiting room. The distinctive purple and lime-green banners were also on community information notice boards everywhere.

In the spring of 2015, Anita noticed a spot – not a mole – a spot that didn't seem to want to go away. Being sensible, she went to the doctor to get it checked out. The doctor allayed her fears and stated that there was nothing to worry about. More time went by and still the spot wouldn't disappear, having a sort of sugary textured scab that never quite healed. She decided to get a second opinion. The confirmation came through, it was skin cancer – Squamous Cell Carcinoma.

The delivery of the news came on a calm, quiet sort of day; blue skies and a little warm sunshine. The devastation Anita heard ringing in her head and ears was, however, deafening. Anita found that she had an inability to hear what the consultant said next other than the single sentence containing the word 'cancer'. As she left the building and stepped out into the sunshine she knew one thing, she needed a drink; a drink to help with the shock. She knew the best drink for her was a sherry, a Tio Pepe to be exact. An old fashioned tipple, but one her grandmother was often heard saying, 'sherry for shock'.

The pub across the road from the hospital looked like the perfect answer. Her husband had softly mentioned that he understood she was ill, but it was getting on for dinner time. 'Blow dinner, blow the time of day, blow everything' she said to herself. She needed time to think and to try and digest what she had just been told. The news she had been given had lost all detail other than she had cancer.

Anita almost fell through the door, not noticing the raised door jam or the large sign above the door stating 'Mind the Step'. She was only saved by the grasp of her husband steadying her as he quickly steered her to a table in the corner before her legs buckled. Regaining some composure once seated, Anita's thoughts were interrupted by a very young waitress sporting purple hair, piercings in her nose, eyebrow, and at least twenty in both ears. The young girl shuffled nervously from one foot to the other, Anita wondered if she had picked up on the tension or if maybe her shoes were uncomfortable, but she didn't really care. She heard her husband order a pint for himself, his voice sounded as if in a dream; discernible but way off in the distance, almost like an echo. Her own mind was a deep, dense fog.

The young girl asked her twice what she would like to drink, Anita tried to get herself together and answered brightly, 'Tio Pepe sherry, a large one please.' The girl's face was a blank; there was again silence between the three people. Anita inexplicably felt a surge of annoyance. 'Sherry please, sherry.' She said loudly, as if bellowing might change the girl's expression. The waitress looked no different, the blank face just blinked at the space somewhere above Anita's head. Now was not a person who lost her temper readily, but she felt anger rising.

'What's that?' the purple-haired girl muttered. She was genuinely confused.

'Sherry, sherry, sherry,' she snapped incredulously. Anita could feel her husband's gaze burning into her from the left side, but she was unable to help herself. She had become helpless to stop herself from displaying her irritation.

In her mind's eye, she saw herself move in slow motion. She leapt up, kicked her chair back – kung fu style – and barged past the waitress, running towards the bar. Hitching up her skirt above her knees, and in a beautifully orchestrated movement that Starsky and Hutch would have been proud of, she launched herself onto the bar. Splayed along the length of the bar, she tilted her head towards the optics and leant back. The whisky, vodka, and gin bottles gleamed in the sunlight. Placing her head beneath the optics, she pressed the release for the vodka and allowed the liquid to fall directly into her mouth, taking great gulps. She could feel the burning liquid make its way through her body, and with its progress, her muscles relax.

In reality, Anita felt herself regain control, smile at the purple-haired girl, and allow her shoulders to relax. The waitress was standing in front of her, now looking bored and chewing on her pen, still awaiting a reply, but looking like she couldn't care less if it never came.

In a smooth, soothing voice Anita smiled and said, 'I'll have a large Pinot Grigio then.' From the corner of her eye, Anita could just make out her husband visibly lighten up and relax. Explosion averted, Anita smiled to herself, grandma's remedy could wait until they got home.

Anon

Drip, Drip, Drip.

Maggie had decided that she would make the most of a good day. When she considered 'the most' of a day now, in comparison to the hectic pace of what was her previous life, it entailed a single trip to the local supermarket. Even getting herself ready was a snail-paced affair, but Maggie was now accustomed to it. She had learnt to listen to her body and its energy levels and act accordingly.

With her headscarf wrapped bandana style and make-up applied, Maggie was ready to go. Sam, her pug dog, looked up at her hopefully. 'Not just yet Sam, maybe later though.' Maggie smiled lovingly at his little hopeful expression. Even Sam had adjusted to this new life of sporadic short walks, plenty of relaxing and the very occasional outing. It was a little different to the adventures that Maggie and Sam had in the past. Hikes up Snowdonia with Sam spending a little time in Maggie's rucksack, head poking out from the top enjoying the fresh bracing air. He only had short legs after all, and he did so enjoy the comfort of the warm fleece wrap. There were long walks along beaches in Norfolk with the surf touching his toes, and Maggie throwing stones for him to bring back and lay at her feet.

Sam had watched his mistress shed so many tears for such a long time, but she had always smiled when he had attempted to lick them away. He knew how to cheer her up and was happy to be there for his best friend. Sam returned to his cosy basket surrounded by his soft toys; he could wait for a walk. He watched Maggie gather up her keys and close the door behind her. Another nap was the perfect pastime until Maggie returned.

The sun was shining, and Maggie was enjoying the feeling of warmth on her face. She couldn't help but smile; today was definitely a good day. Birds were singing their songs in the hedges and the trees she passed on the short walk to the shops. Maggie felt her nose twitching; she had suffered from hayfever in the past, but since the chemotherapy she had been symptom-free. She was guessing the treatment had pretty much killed off any other mildly irritating condition in its wake. The twitching got worse, she felt like a hyperactive rabbit, her nose seemed to have a will of its own.

Inside the supermarket, Maggie hoped the twitching would stop. Her attention diverted for the moment, she chose some fruit; plums, apples, a coconut, blueberries, and strawberries. With these in her basket she headed over to the salad section. It was early, and the supermarket was fairly quiet. The lettuce she picked up looked like it might have already been washed; there being a couple of small droplets on its bright green, shiny leaves. When she leant forward to choose a cucumber, there were a couple of droplets on it too. Maggie looked towards the ceiling of the supermarket, wondering if there was a leak or a faulty air conditioning vent, but there was nothing. Wiping away the moisture from the items, she continued around the various displays.

It wasn't long before Maggie began to slow down and she knew her energy levels were lowering, so she made her way to the checkout. The half dozen items she had were not heavy, and she was looking forward to the gentle walk home; happy with herself and her efforts.

Suddenly there was another drip on her hand, a great sploshing one this time. Again she looked up to see where this mysterious liquid was coming from, it was almost as if it were following her around the supermarket. Tilting her head backwards and looking up, she tasted something on her top lip.

It was then that Maggie knew it was her nose that had been running the whole time. All the way around the supermarket her nose had been dripping like a leaky tap. In a panic, she patted herself down but could not find a single tissue; her face was burning with embarrassment. With her hand over the lower part of her face, she apologised profusely to the lady at the till, 'I'm so sorry, I don't have a single tissue.' The lady smiled at her and produced a packet of tissues from under the counter. 'They tell you you'll lose the hair from your head, but don't always mention anywhere else. And when do we ever think about nose hair?', she laughed. It was only then that Maggie noticed the lady was sporting a navy headscarf, it matched her uniform perfectly. Maggie was so used to seeing people around her with various forms of head gear and wigs that she hadn't even acknowl-edged the cashier's own.

Maggie took a couple of tissues and laughed out loud at how much her nose had been run-ning. 'Just be grateful you don't have a cold', laughed the lady at the till, 'the last time I had one, I had to stay indoors for a week.' She said, chuckling. Maggie giggled to herself all the way home. She wondered how keen Sam would have been to lick her face today.

Susan & Casey
Marks Out Of Ten

Diane and John were completely shocked when they received the news that Diane had hormone sensitive breast cancer. Diane was thirty-four and the proud mother of two young boys, Luke – two and Zach – five. When the news was delivered, it was completely unexpected, and they went along to the follow-up appointment as a family. Little Luke was clambering all over his Dad's legs; desperate to touch, play, and dismantle anything, as only a two-year-old can. Zach was five and although a little quieter, he too was fascinated by the whole visit to the hospital. The bright lights, nurses in uniforms, and important looking people in white coats and suits going about their business, transfixed him.

John was the first to react, his anger boiled within him; it was evident to Diane, in his eyes as he looked at the consultant, and because the colour rising up through his neck was getting redder and redder. She looked from one man to the other, unable to gauge how she was going to deal with them and the news she had just been given. A nurse appeared, as if from nowhere, offering to take the children to the adjoining room. John's first sentence when his children were out of earshot was completely accusatory, 'You're telling me that he's two, he's five, their mother is only thirty-four, I'm thirty-six and she has cancer!' He was pointing at the area where his children had stood and then jabbing his finger in the direction of the consultant in a threatening manner as he spat out the words. Diane saw the situation deteriorate in front of her eyes and knew she had to act fast.

'John, let's hear the rest of what he has to say.' He turned towards his wife when he felt her hand on his arm. His eyes filled with tears, but she held his gaze steadily. Diane saw the anger pass as quickly as it had arrived. The consultant went on to explain the treatment they would proceed with once they had run a few more tests; only then could they consider a prognosis. The time they spent in the overlit room with the man in the suit and the nurse who had returned their children, seemed to Diane to be interminable.

When they finally left the hospital and joined the five o'clock Cambridge traffic, there was silence in the car. Luke and Zach had fallen asleep in their car seats by the time they approached the first roundabout heading out of town. Diane and John were lost in their own thoughts, but their hands remained touching throughout the short journey home.

Two weeks later, all the results were in from the various tests were in. A treatment schedule had been agreed upon, and all measures were in place for help with the children and everyday life for the family. Diane was a lady of faith; over the two weeks she had prayed for the strength to see herself and her family through the coming months. She woke one morning a couple of weeks after the fateful consultation, and found she had a new strength within her. She felt capable of anything. It was from that day on that she made it her mission to pass on this positivity to her friends, family, and children.

The treatments started and it wasn't long before Diane's hair had fallen out completely, but the family was functioning well and a new normalcy took over. Diane looked forward to the day when she felt her old self again, but knew she had a long road to get there. She had never felt ill at any point prior to her diagnosis, only the detected lump signified her condition. The treatments made her feel far worse than she could have imagined, but she held on tight to the knowledge that they were, in the long run, all essential in making her better.

Diane made sure she tried to venture out on her 'good days'. She was self-conscious of her appearance and had tried a wig, but she felt even more uncomfortable, and John always said she 'rocked the bald look'. So she had made the decision early on not to cover up her hair loss. It was this decision that led to a game created by John and Diane to help her cope with other people's reactions to her appearance. Diane knew she couldn't explain to each and every stranger that she was getting better, and that they shouldn't worry. This only made her worry more, and she knew she had to think of herself and her health, instead of allowing herself to be too affected by others. John was adamant she couldn't allow herself to get upset or worried on behalf of other people, she had to concentrate on herself.

It began one day when the family was out shopping together with the two children running around happily. Diane noticed a woman staring her way, looking from the children to John and then to Diane. Diane felt that she needed to tell the woman she was okay, everything was going to be fine. The expression the woman wore was one of shock and pity. Diane knew she couldn't let it be of concern to her, but she felt guilty nonetheless. John came up with a game, and it seemed to help Diane. Initially, she felt they were being harsh but it proved to be her saviour. If they saw it, John and Diane would score a person's reaction out of ten. It was never a malicious undertaking, rather a coping mechanism for them, so they didn't take on more anxiety. It also meant Diane did not feel like she had to reassure a complete stranger that she was, in fact, getting better.

They began to have fun, and realised if they appeared to be fine and laughing then others picked up on it. There were some though who warranted a full ten on their imaginary score cards, particularly when they were out as a family. This was especially evident when John was walking along with their toddler in a pushchair and a five-year-old Zach hanging off his or Diane's arm. Diane and John would call to each other 5…7…no definite 10, referring to their 'pity scale'. "We may need to go and buy them some tissues", John would say.

Taking the edge off things with a playful approach meant they could not help everyone, but being able to make light of a reaction helped them through the journey they were living. John and Diane knew the rule for living with cancer was – 'there are no rules' – you get through it the way you choose, and that is exactly what they did.

Inspired by Michelle

Is it a Bird? Is it a Plane?

Suzy found her diagnosis of breast cancer to be a huge inconvenience, almost as much as a worrying shock. She was a practical woman; a successful businesswoman with a busy PR practice in London. She lived in the home counties in a quiet village, which allowed her an escape from London's busy hustle and bustle. Her home was a handsome four bedroom detached mock Tudor affair, with an easy to maintain garden and smart paved driveway.

Finding the small, pea-sized lump in her left breast brought with it irritation and an overwhelming sense of annoyance. She simply didn't have the time for this. The consultant was swift to confirm her fears; scans showed she had discovered her lump early, and her treatment would be a lumpectomy followed by chemotherapy. The side effects of the chemotherapy were explained, and dates were booked for treatment to commence.

With a bit of juggling and the hiring of some extra staff, Suzy felt as organised with a treatment schedule and how her life would proceed afterwards as, she guessed, could be possible. She explained in a matter-of-fact-manner about her diagnosis to her staff; feeling she owed it to them to both put them in the picture and at ease with the new arrangements. She was touched by their response, and felt that when she was well again, she would perhaps spend a little more time with them all on a more social level. She knew she was often aloof and could be standoffish from time to time.

The treatments went well, but Suzy was amazed at how quickly the side effects took their toll, she was completely bald in a very short period of time. To cheer herself up she bought a very stylish and expensive wig. It looked fabulous, she was pleased with the result, and was beginning to feel a little more like her usual self. Suzy also found she was having to learn to take herself a little less seriously; to laugh at herself from time to time, and to see the funnier side of life.

This was never more apparent than on the occasion she was having her chemotherapy and needed to go to the toilet. The larger disabled toilet was occupied and she had to take her dispenser, which was much taller than her and had four wheels which appeared to roll in any direction other than the way you wanted, into the standard sized toilet. Trying to manoeuvre herself, the wheelie thing, and remove her lower body garments simultaneously, she quickly realised she had almost contorted herself into a granny knot. Having then caught her reflection in the mirror positioned over what was possibly the smallest hand basin known to man, she couldn't help but laugh. She resembled a badly wrapped, oversized parcel with an I.V. line criss-crossing over her face, and for whatever reason, she now had an arm suspended in the air over her head, giving the appearance of a somewhat worse-for-wear marionette. At this point she was laughing loudly at herself as she managed to shuffle towards the toilet door and slide the lock, allowing the door to fall open just a crack.

It was her raucous laughter that caught the attention of one of the ward nurses. Although it was obvious she required assistance, she was unable to explain anything through her laughter. The nurse saw immediately what had happened and a full ten minutes later Suzy had been unravelled, repositioned in the disabled toilet, and was able to sort herself out.

Suzy felt capable of returning to work after a time. She craved the buzz of the office and the business's demanding clients. In typical fashion, the morning of her return to work she slept through her alarms. Rushing to catch the train at the station nearby, she quickly applied her make-up and newly acquired wig. Pleased with her appearance, she jumped in a taxi; not wanting to tire herself out by the walk to the station.

The train arrived within a couple of minutes of purchasing her return ticket. The wind had picked up, and Suzy was glad of the warmth of the already full carriage. She stood for part of the journey before a seat became available at Tottenham Hale.

As it passed through a tunnel, Suzy marvelled at how different the person looking back at her from the reflection in the train window was now. After ten minutes, Liverpool Street Station came into view. Suzy was both excited and nervous to return to her office. The PR firm had taken years to build up, and she was proud of her accomplishments. Now she felt more proud of herself than ever. In her eyes, her cancer had been removed, and she was now 'recovering from having cancer', not someone who was 'suffering with cancer'.

As she stepped out of Liverpool Street Station and onto the wide pavement, the wind was gusting through the narrow streets. Suddenly, Suzy's head was cold, really cold; she knew straightaway what had happened. At that exact moment, she heard a shriek behind her. Turning, she saw a small man in a business suit, arms flailing wildly, looking for all the world like he was trying to wrestle some sort of furry creature. She couldn't make out if it was a small cat or dog. It was blonde in colour, and slightly circular in shape. The man was squealing in a high-pitched voice, very clearly disturbed by the unprovoked attack. The animal looked like it was stuck to him, attacking him. Suzy quickly identified the animal.

Straightening her skirt, adjusting her suit jacket, and with her head held high, she headed over to the man. She snatched the furry object from him, patted it down neatly, and then pulled it onto her head; hoping against hope she had at least placed it on the right way round. Then she stalked off, in what she prayed was a confident and purposeful manner, in the direction of her office.

By the time the lift reached Bryce Public Relations, Suzy was once more laughing to herself and made a mental note to always carry extra double-sided toupe tape. It was an interesting start to her first day back at work.

Margaret

Catch That!

Amy had completed the whole treatment for her latest visit from the cancer monster, this was how she liked to refer to the recurrence of the disease. She had been unfortunate in having cancer strike in various parts of her body over the years, including bladder, kidney, and the latest was breast. She felt that she was now a bit of an old hand at taking on the necessary treatments, she had tried most of them at least once.

For her breast cancer she had a double mastectomy, she had no intention of taking any chances and it was agreed upon without hesitation. She had decided not to have any reconstructive surgery for the time being, and wore prosthetic implants in her underwear. Amy was simply grateful to be given another chance.

Two years on, and Amy's lust for life was as evident as ever. She and her husband were regulars at the local gym, enjoyed going out for evenings dancing, and there wasn't a party that she didn't get an invite to. Amy made it her mission to make the very most of every day, even when she wasn't always feeling one hundred percent. When a close friend and her husband suggested a holiday in Spain, Amy jumped at the idea. A villa was booked, along with flights, and a hire car; Amy couldn't wait.

Shopping for clothes was already a passion for Amy, but with a holiday to shop for she took shopping to a whole new level. Her husband despaired as to how much luggage they were going to have to take, but took it all in good humour. He loved seeing his wife getting so much pleasure out of life and he knew they were going to have a great time. Having been friends with the couple for many years, the foursome were completely comfortable in each other's company, all being of similar ages; and though Amy had never had children, her friend Susie's were all grown up and had families of their own. Already close, the foursome had grown even closer throughout Amy's treatments.

On the morning of the departure, the four were enjoying breakfast before heading out to the airport. Amy had made sure all her medication was correctly labelled, document supported, and in all the required measures. When everyone was ready they headed off to the airport, which wasn't too far away. The journey took only twenty minutes in a taxi, and the group were deposited at the terminal building. Amy couldn't hide her excitement about going on holiday. They had always had short breaks away, but with all the treatments Amy had endured, they had never been able to get anything more than a few days here and there. For years they had always been in the U.K., as she wasn't fit enough to travel any greater distance. Having been given the go ahead by her doctors, this was to be the first trip abroad in over ten years. For Amy it felt like the very first time, and she was determined to make the most of every minute.

The group arrived a little early for their flight and decided a celebratory drink would be a great way to start the holiday. A bottle of champagne was ordered for the ladies and ice-cold beer for the men. It was only just past noon, but they all agreed they had more reason than ever to celebrate. In no time their flight was called and the happy foursome were on their way.

Landing in the brilliant sunshine and feeling its warmth instantly made Amy feel better than ever. She had no plans for the days to come other than simply enjoy her time with the like-minded people she loved.

Days were spent lounging around the pool, sunning herself like the native lizards, swimming, and enjoying as much of the Spanish experience as possible. Amy was determined to make the very most of every moment. She loved the feel of the sun on her skin. She sampled as much of the local delicacies as possible; from baked baby clams to delicious suckling pig. The couples enjoyed trips to the coast, vineyards, cheese making farms, and tried at least one different restaurant or tapas bar a day.

Amy tried to make sure she got as much rest as possible in between activities, but her lust for life was boundless. The group joked that it was her, out of the four, who had the most energy anyway; and they were all quite glad when she decided she needed a rest and would take herself off to the cool of the villa for a nap.

It was while they were out shopping in the nearest mall, with its amazing collection of shops and boutiques, that Amy picked up a leaflet for the Aquavelis Water Park in nearby Torre Del Mar. That was it, that was going to be Amy's next conquest; her husband and friends thought she was completely mad. 'Don't you think we are just a teensy bit past it?' laughed Josh, Amy's husband. 'We'll be the oldest ones there', laughed her friend Susie. 'I need to do it, you all said this was a trip of discovery and recovery, and for my next discovery I would like to hurtle down a slide, screaming like a banshee,' she laughed. It was settled, the next day would be "water park day". Amy fell asleep smiling to herself that night, like a child, she couldn't wait for the following day to come.

The water park was busy with large family groups, teenagers hanging around in groups trying their best to look cool and unaffected by each other's presence. Amy felt the same surge of excitement she had felt as a child when visiting fairgrounds or the anticipation leading up to Christmas. Her heart was pounding as the four made their way to the top of the first slide. The men went first, claiming they wanted to be at the bottom to catch their spouses when it was their turn to come down the slide. In reality, the two men had reverted to their own childhoods and were keen to take the plunge down the slide.

The water was pumping down the length of the brightly coloured tubes keeping the riders moving at break-neck speed along the slippery surface. In a moment, both men had disappeared into the darkness of the first hairpin bend. Amy and Susie readied themselves at the top of the slide, waiting for the go-ahead from the lifeguards to launch themselves down the ride. On the count of three the two friends jettisoned themselves down the slide to the first bend. Amy was squealing with delight as she hurtled past others, who were now queuing up the steep hill to take the ride. She guessed it must have been quite a sight seeing a middle aged woman sporting a psychedelic bikini zipping past at lightning speed, making more noise than anybody else.

As Amy approached the final bend she felt the water surge behind her, and laughed out loud at the sheer exhileration she felt at being weightless, as she became airborne at the end of the slide. As she was mid-air something caught her eye for a split second, it was opaque with a silvery sheen to it in the sunlight. As quick as she saw it, it was gone. She heard a familiar voice yell, 'catch that!', as she plunged into the pool at the bottom of the slide.

At the moment she found her feet in the plunge pool, she was joined by her laughing friends and husband. In one smooth discreet motion Marcus, Susie's husband, had pinged Amy's bikini strap and plopped something in the cup. 'You'll be missing that', he laughed. Amy thought she may collapse, laughing as the other three regaled the story of the middle-aged woman bombing down the slide, arms and legs all over the place, a false breast flying high into the air, and being beautifully caught by a man with a look of concentration on his face worthy of any fielder participating in an England versus Australia cricket match at Lords.

Jan
Groundhog Day Radio

Jan was not looking forward to the next six weeks. She was due radiotherapy every day including weekends. The dose had been explained to her as being gradually increased but she was under no illusion, she would soon become very ill.

The treatment started on a Monday, and her husband drove the well-rehearsed route to Addenbrooke's Hospital in Cambridge. The couple tried to make light of the situation; how long they would be repeating the journey, how many miles they would clock up, how many stairs they would climb, cups of tea they would drink, how many times the same questions would be asked verifying name, date of birth etc., before the radio would be administered.

By the end of the first week, Jan was getting the routine pat down. She had made friends with others undergoing the same treatment schedule and others who were on different regimes, but all with the same goal, to beat cancer. Jan also knew her nurse's names, and by the end of the second week she had memorised their shift schedules, knew about their families, how old their children were, and where they had gone or were going on holiday.

Jan began to feel the effects of her treatment, and she started to feel unwell, but continued with the schedule knowing it would get worse before she got better; the hours, days, and weeks began to blur for both Jan and her husband. The trips to the hospital were marked with the passing of the same landmarks each and every day. The drive was made almost on auto-pilot. She visited the same room, the same chair, and looked out of the same window. The routine reminded her of a film she had once watched called Groundhog Day, where the day restarted the same every single day; with the same events, conversations, and interactions. Jan felt she was actually living that film plot, just a different scenario.

One morning, Jan was stopped as she was leaving the treatment suite. The receptionist asked, as she did from time, to time when Jan's next session was. The answer was always the same: same time, same place the following day.

The receptionist checked her appointment book, flipping pages back and forth. A smile spread across her face. 'Nope Jan, actually, you have no more appointments, that's it! Your treatments have finished.' Her smile stretched from ear-to-ear.

Jan felt her body relax and she beamed back at the lady behind the desk. 'That's it? I'm done? I'm really done?' Jan was delighted, exhausted, but delighted. She spent a few minutes saying goodbye to all the staff, patients, and the friends she had shared six weeks of her life with. She didn't expect to feel so emotional and was caught off guard by the love and affection shown by everyone. Jan's husband had been under the same illusion as Jan, and he was equally delighted to learn his wife's treatments had come to an end. Their own personal 'Groundhog Day' had finally stopped. The drive home that day was filled with laughter, relief and renewed hope for the future.

Fion

Back to front, Top to Bottom

Fi was amazed at just how much her body had changed. At first she was saddened, so much so, that she thought she might seek some support to help her through her feelings. It was only when she went to a local support group that she found others experiencing the same emotions, and she gained renewed strength and perspective, and became more accepting of her body and all it had been through.

Fi had undergone a procedure, an LD operation, where a section of flesh and muscle from her back was used to create a new breast. When the surgery was completed, Fi was pleased with the results and would comment that she was now "back-to-front". She would happily accredit it for anything, from forgetfulness to unexplained bouts of retail therapy (which often resulted in her returning unwanted items, which then facilitated another wander around the shops). If she was getting cross she would yell, 'you're getting right on my back'. This was her polite way of actually saying, 'you're getting right on my tit'; and those who knew her well, knew exactly what she meant. Fi laughed along with everyone, enjoying the double meaning.

She enjoyed sharing stories of talented surgeons creating body enhancements from various other body parts. One of Fi's favourites was one lady's recollection of her breast being created from a section of her midriff. It was only when the lady in question's hair began to grow back, that she experienced hair growth in some odd places and the hairs that grew in the 'odd' places; were short, coarse, and bore no resemblance to the soft downy re-growth on her head. Feeling she needed to see someone about the hair, she made an appointment to see her consultant fearing her hormones may have created another issue other than cancer.

It was only on the morning of her appointment while in the shower that she burst out laughing and couldn't stop. The scar on her abdomen explained everything she needed to know; the hair would have been completely natural in the location of her scar. Toweling herself dry, she went to the phone and dialled the number for her consultant to cancel the appointment. As she hung up the receiver a quote popped into her head, 'Where'er you be let the hair grow free'. When she next went to her group meeting and spoke to her Macmillan nurse, she took great pleasure in regaling them of her discovery. As it turned out, as is so often the case, she was not the only patient to have discovered hair in strange and unusual places.

Double Up Dolly

Inspired by Anita

Dolly was on a downer; she had been feeling ill from the side effects of her chemotherapy for so long, it had almost overtaken the fact that she had been diagnosed with breast cancer. She hadn't had a single symptom and the detection had been made on a purely routine mammogram. The cancer was now gone, it had been cut out, it was no longer there, and yet she felt so wretched. A double mastectomy had taken care of the tumour and any possibility of another, and she was eternally grateful.

Though none of this took away the fact that she was feeling so poorly. It was exhausting to be sick all the time; feeling too exhausted to be bothered with anything or anyone. Her throat was so sore, that even if she wanted to she could barely get anything down. Dolly was tired of not feeling like her normal self and it was getting her down.

The morning started out like any other, slowly. Dolly had to talk herself into getting out of bed. She could have quite easily laid in bed all day, but she knew that was a slippery slope and ultimately did her no good, other than make her all the more depressed. It was at this point, wallowing in her mood, that Dolly noticed something she hadn't seen in what seemed like an age. On the bedroom floor was a bright shaft of light stretching from one side of the room to the other.

The shaft of light originated from the side of the blind at the bedroom window. Dolly could not believe it was true? Slowly, she pulled back the duvet and placed her feet on the floor. Walking towards the window the carpet was feeling warm under her feet. As she lifted the blind, she was delighted to see she had guessed right. It was a beautiful sunny morning, bright blue sky, not a cloud, and Dolly stood enjoying the warmth of the sunlight streaming in. She couldn't help but be comforted and her mood lifted.

After standing for a considerable time listening to the birds singing and watching a tractor in the far field behind her house, Dolly formulated a plan. She was not going to let today go to waste; she was going to be as cheerful as possible. Flinging open the door of her wardrobe she chose a floral dress in bright colours, shoes, and accessories. Checking the calendar, she saw it was a Brafternoon Ladies Day, and she had never intended on going. Now she changed her mind, she would go, she would meet people, and she would do her damnedest to enjoy herself. She chose her prettiest underwear, and it was as she was dressing that she chuckled to herself. She was going to have a little fun.

Being out in the sunshine, feeling its warmth, and the brightness making trees, grass, and flowers look almost neon in their brilliance of colour. Every living thing looked as if it were illuminated from within. Every now and then Dolly would catch a glimpse of her reflection and smile to herself, today was a special day, Dolly could feel it.

The drawing room at the country hotel where the Brafternoon group met was buzzing. The sunshine had brought out more attendees than Dolly had ever seen. The scene looked like a garden party with the French doors flung wide open onto the sun terrace and gardens. Large umbrellas were dotted about offering just enough shade.

As Dolly walked in, Anita, the hostess did a double take. Dolly smiled brightly at her. 'Goodness Dolly, you look fabulous.' Dolly made her way over to Anita, then pulled her to a quiet part of the room. Checking that no one was looking, Dolly pulled the strap of her dress to one side allowing Anita to see a glimpse of bra and revealing her secret accessories. Tucked into the bra was her prosthetic breast, but Dolly had made a little adjustment to her look.

Today Dolly had doubled up on her implants. She was, for today, Brafternoon's very own Dolly Parton. 'Thought I'd cheer myself up' she laughed as she proudly sauntered off to join the others getting drinks and making their way to the gardens.

Lesley

Brenda

Anita

Susan

Susan & Casey

Jan J

Myer

TISSUES

Clare

Sadie

Ian

Jenny, Brenda & Diane

Michelle

Julie

Michelle

Kay

Jo

Anon

Hair There, Really?

Mel had been distraught when her hair fell out in great clumps, not long after she started her cancer treatment.

Try as she might she couldn't stop the inevitable. She looked up every suggested lotion, potion and cold cap method but nothing worked for her. When her treatment had finished, ironically, it was waiting for her hair to reappear that became all-consuming. When the delicate fuzz of regrowth made its much longed for appearance she was ecstatic. Her friends and family rejoiced in her return to her old, upbeat self.

Every morning Mel would gently wash the soft downy hair. Before her diagnosis of cancer Mel had warm brown hair but she could already see the new hair was coming through blonde. She had always toyed with having a change of colour and it looked like nature had taken the decision for her.

Mel waited patiently for her hair to grow. Like anything truly longed for the waiting seemed to take an eternity. When her hair was about an inch long all over and she looked less bald and more 'cropped' Mel decided to leave her hat at home and venture out with dramatic earrings or a vibrant scarf, she was proud of her new hair and happy to show it off, everyday feeling stronger and a little more like her old self.

One day Mel was at the bathroom sink marvelling at the now gentle, golden waves all over her head, her hair was still short but she loved it. As the sunlight streamed through the bathroom window filling the room with almost white light Mel noticed something fluttering on the side of her face. It disappeared, and then as a breeze rose from the small open window to her left she saw it again.

It was a single, fine, long hair, about three inches long. Mel swiped at it thinking it was a loose hair having attached itself probably to a piece of clothing or a towel. It didn't budge, as she made a definitive grab for it she realised, in horror, it was in fact attached to her, not only to her, but to her chin!

Yes, the one place where her hair had grown super fast was the last place she had wanted it or even thought was possible.

Even though she was mortified by her discovery, she had to laugh; she was actually quite proud of the hair, it was a thread of hope that her hair would grow back fully.

Plucking the wayward hair Mel carefully wrapped it in a tissue and put it in her bedside drawer, still chuckling to herself she could wait to regale the story. Checking her appearance once more she left her home for work. She was careful to check regularly, in case there were any more stray hair poking from ears or worse still her nose, laughing to herself every time she did so.

Margaret
Knitting, Not Such An Innocent Hobby

With so much sitting around in Chemotherapy, new hobbies can often be taken up, something to while away the hours the treatments can take. This was definitely the case for Margaret's group, and knitting was the chosen 'in thing'. The crowd who shared her chemotherapy session were a sassy bunch who loved a good laugh at just about anything. They would banter with the nursing staff, and try their very best to make the most of their time spent together.

There were a few male nurses on the ward, and they were always good sports with whatever was going on. The chemotherapy sessions were almost looked forward to, not by any means the treatment aspect, but certainly the company and camaraderie within the group.

The patients had been knitting for some time; there were always balls of coloured yarn dangling from chairs or spilling out of knitting bags. The gentle clickity-click sound of knitting needles succumbed to busy fingers. Everyone was looking forward to showing off the fruits of their labour.

When the time finally came to show their wares, everyone was looking forward with great anticipation. There was a buzz about the group; were there going to be multi-coloured blankets, baby booties, hats, gloves, and scarves? Everybody was keeping things very much to themselves.

It was a good thing the male nurses were such good fun and happy to share a joke, as when all the knitted items were revealed one patient had very carefully, and very kindly knitted Willie Warmers. Suffice to say, nobody could top this for entertainment value alone. The laughter could be heard throughout the unit. It is safe to say it pays to have a good sense of humour when dealing with cancer patients and carers.

No nurses were harmed or offended in the making or regaling of this story, I am reliably informed.

Julie
Bowel Class not Bowls Class

With so many side effects from two different types of cancer so far, Julie was used to some re-education; and learning to live with her body. It was only when she found that her bowels – which had been an issue even prior to her cancer diagnosis – started to be affected by her medication, that she was recommended a 'Bowel Re-education Class'. At first, she thought her Macmillan nurse was joking with her, but it was true; there was help and assistance for anyone who was experiencing difficulties in the toilet department.

A week after talking to her nurse, and after spending a particularly miserable weekend at home unable to venture out as the pain and discomfort of not being able to go to the toilet at all, and by Monday was feeling like she was going to explode, she contacted her treatment centre. She found out when the next bowel therapy session was scheduled, she had just a couple of days to wait. By the time the morning of the session came, Julie was more than ready. Her discomfort was almost unbearable and she knew if she didn't do anything, it was likely she would have to be admitted to hospital for manual assistance. A non-too-pleasant experience and one she was definitely keen to avoid.

Julie arrived for the session and was comforted to see she was not alone, in fact there was quite a full class already in the waiting room. Julie took a seat, and she almost burst out laughing as another person taking the session was the double of the late Barbara Woodhouse, dog trainer extraordinaire. Neat haircut, sensible shoes, a tweed skirt, with a no-nonsense expression fixed firmly on her face. Julie had watched many a programme featuring the canine genius bringing unruly four-legged furry friends in line, and then rewarding them only when they had mastered her commands.

The attendees filed into the large, airy room, which was filled with multi-coloured yoga mats, all spaced equally apart. In one firmly spoken command, each mat was claimed by a delegate.

Julie listened to the instructions for relaxation exercises, visualisation, and techniques of how to approach the tricky business of going to the toilet. At first, the embarrassment was palpable, but as the session progressed everyone seemed to relax, and what Julie was hearing made sense. She had never considered 'pushing only from the hips', but it made perfect sense now. The relaxation techniques were already beginning to work, when the mechanics of the body were explained, and how everything from food, mood, anxiety, as well as medication, can affect the simplest of bodily functions; it was hardly surprising that she was having difficulties and things become stalled. A body, she was informed, cannot be trained to do things on command; unlike a dog thought Julie.

Julie rid herself of the image of the therapist standing in front of her enunciating in a clear voice 'Sit' accompanied by the legendary Barbara Woodhouse arm gesture, which every dog obeyed regardless. She stifled a laugh at the image of all the attendees sitting obediently. By the end of the session, Julie felt relaxed and more in control than ever. Getting home, and in the comfort of her own bathroom, Julie was granted the release she had been longing for.

She vowed never again to mock the benefits of her 'Bowel Class', in fact, she would go on a 'Bowel Class' promotional tour, starting with her next support group meeting, she was a convert.

Anon

The Swimming Hat Brigade

Helen had succumbed to her treatment. She had good days, and she had bad days. One thing was constant however, her support network. Her girls, Helen's Heroes, were always there for her. Some days she felt like she needed to be surrounded by their constant babble, raucous laughter, and often insane anecdotes; and others she preferred no company or the company of just one. Helen's Heroes was made up of the women she had met through playgroups, having children, living in the same neighbourhood, work, life in general and some being single mums like her; all having shared life's experiences with her at various points. Dealing with cancer was no exception. As soon as Helen had broken the news, the Heroes rallied around.

Helen made the decision to have her hair cut short, having sported long tresses for quite some time. She had also decided to try the 'cold cap' method while having chemotherapy in the hope of avoiding hair loss. This entailed a gel-filled cap being worn before, during, and after chemotherapy. It was by no means the most glamorous of looks, but one Helen was going to give a go. A girl's night in was planned at Helen's house, and a theme was decided, unbeknown to her. With drinks and nibbles organised, Helen waited for the arrival of her dearest friends.

The doorbell rang, and Helen completed one last check of her appearance in the mirror. She was slowly beginning to get used to her shorn appearance and her hair was surviving for the moment. The lamplight around the front door was reflecting something as she opened it and for a moment she was blinded. It was then she saw each of her friends; as they stepped over the threshold they all sported shiny, hairless heads. Helen couldn't help but laugh at the multi-coloured heads. Everyone was sporting a swimming cap of one description or another; faces pulled tight at obscure angles, and none looking like themselves. It was safe to say that Helen sported the longest hairstyle that evening, and the group laughed long and hard into the early hours at each other's bizarre appearance. The photos of their escapades were circulated and enjoyed for weeks to come. Helen couldn't help but laugh to herself whenever she remembered her group of friends and how they made her laugh so much that night.

Anita C

H.H.C. (Happy Herceptin Cattle)

Anita was still trying to come to terms with the new person she had become. It was an undeniable fact that cancer had changed her. Although some would say this was inevitable, it was so much easier to brush the emotional as well as the physical change off as being 'one of those things', unless you are the person actually living it. Treatment days were often anxious times accompanied by their own levels of stress. She had been prescribed the drug Herceptin, and had to attend hospital to have it administered. It was delivered by special courier and was administered immediately.

On this particular day Anita was feeling a little low, but as she walked into the treatment room her spirits lifted slightly. Everyone, from the nursing staff to the patients, had the ability to bring the room alive with positivity. They were all there for the same goal; Herceptin was going to help make them better. Looking around Anita couldn't help but smile to herself. All of the patients were either hooked up to saline drips, which helped to keep them hydrated and keep vital veins open for the life giving treatment, or in the process of being fitted with I.Vs in readiness for the much anticipated delivery.

Information drifted through that the delivery was going to be a little late, which had the knock-on effect of numerous loo breaks. The room took on a cattle market atmosphere as overloaded bladders, skipping rope length I.V. systems with accompanying wheeled monitors, and nurses attempting to assist with the great contortionist acts that are patients attempting to go to the toilet after waiting in line attached to their I.V.s. There was an almost synchronised dance of patients and nurses keeping the I.V.lines intact, and the assistance of releasing clothing in cubicles that felt no bigger than telephone boxes. It would only take one of the 'cattle' to get the giggles, and there was the distinct possibility of disaster.

Times like these reminded Anita of the camaraderie that is experienced by even the most subdued person. She found her spirits lifted by the end of the treatment sessions, and it was ironic that the benefits of her treatment were not just drug-related. Herceptin was her elixir of life, but the connections and friendships made while sitting amongst others enduring the same treatment and their collective fight with cancer, she knew would last her a lifetime, and she couldn't help but feel grateful.

Jan J
Lucky Black Cats?

There it was again. The small black cat popped its head around the bottom of Jan's bed and regarded her quizzically with its jade eyes. Jan watched as the cat slowly wound its tail around the leg of the bed. All of this may not have been quite so noteworthy if it wasn't for the fact that Jan's current place of residence was the tenth floor of Addenbrooke's Hospital, lovingly referred to the 'Penthouse Suite'.

The cat turned again to look at her for a moment before she saw another small black furry head, and then another. In the space of a couple of minutes Jan had counted five more cats. She burst out laughing when she watched two cats face each other and raise a paw in what appeared to be a feline 'high five', and then proceed to walk up the wall opposite Jan's bed. They were almost to the ceiling and standing perfectly horizontal to the floor, as if it were a normal, everyday occurrence.

Next, two more cats, which had been sitting around the leg of the bed watching with equal fascination as Jan had, at the other wall walking cats, then followed the first pair. Jan could not believe her eyes and turned to talk to the patient in the bed next to her but she was fast asleep, snoring gently, oblivious to the amazing spectacle. Jan returned to watch the final pair follow the other four. By now the first four were upside down on the ceiling, looking like the most unlikely of light fittings.

Halfway up the wall, the final pair of cats turned and faced Jan, and she could have sworn they waved at her with a single paw each before continuing on their way up to join the others. When all of the cats were together again as a group, they sat down in an upside down circle, their tails dangling in midair, resembling furry question marks. By now Jan was laughing so much she was almost crying.

Nurse Cath could see Jan laughing heartily, she felt happy that even though Jan had recently received a bone marrow transplant, she hadn't lost her sense of humour and was clearly finding something amusing. Nurse

Cath made her way to Jan's bed, and smiled at her carer. "Have you ever seen anything like this?" She asked pointing to the ceiling, the cats watching Jan and Nurse Cath with heads to one side. Nurse Cath smiled at her patient, she had worked in Addenbrooke's Oncology department for years now and had listened to many stories of fantastical goings on, particularly during certain treatments, but black cats scaling the walls? Six black cats scaling the walls at that! Yes, that was a new one on her. Hallucinations came in all shapes and sizes, but this was a first.

Clare
Chick
Chick Hair

Clare's six-year-old daughter had been her tonic throughout her cancer journey. Although she had initially struggled with Clare's hair loss – much more so than Clare herself or even her beauty conscious, hairdressing family – she gradually came around to the dramatic change in her mother's appearance.

For the first couple of months, after Clare had finally lost all of her hair, her daughter would insist Clare wear a hat at all times, even indoors. Although on occasion this could prove a little uncomfortable – it was amazing how hot a head could get indoors covered with a hat – Clare was more than happy to oblige anything while her daughter came to terms with things in her mind.

Eventually, the little girl became more and more at ease with her mother's bald head.

When the first regrowth came through, her daughter would pat the warm fuzz calling it 'baby chick, chick hair'.

For Clare, it was a huge comfort that her daughter was adapting to the changes in her life, and doing so with the humour and outlook that only a six-year-old could.

Polly

New Hairdo Grandma?

Polly was spending time with her family, she was staying the weekend with her son and his family. One morning she was getting herself dressed, trying to make herself look presentable, when her grandson toddled in. Chemotherapy had left Polly with hair regrowth that was finally beginning to make an appearance, but until her hair was completely regrown she had decided on a wig which helped her feel a little more comfortable.

As her grandson stood in the doorway, Polly waited for his reaction to seeing her not wearing her wig; it was hanging neatly on the bedpost. This was the first time he had seen her without it and she felt a small rise of anxiety waiting for him to say something. She wondered if her appearance frightened him or made him uneasy, because she had no intention of upsetting her beloved grandchild.

Smiling broadly at his grandma, the little boy tipped his head to one side looking quizzical and then ran toward Polly, his arms outstretched. "New haircut, Grandma?" he asked pointing at the downy regrowth. Polly laughed and scooped the little boy up in her arms. Then he reached for the wig, promptly popped it on his own head, and ran back to the mirror where Polly was sitting. Turning this way and that they laughed at his reflection.

After a few moments, he turned to Polly and declared that although he liked his Grandma's new haircut, he loved the shiny wig. After that morning together Polly's grandson would often ask her if she was feeling well, his concern evident for her. She found his demeanour both touching and charming. As her treatment went on, it was her young grandson who always had the ability to make her smile.

Clare

Is That You Dad? Or Is That Me?

Clare loved looking back at family photos. Although her appearance had changed dramatically, particularly since the diagnosis of cancer, she wasn't in any way bothered by her altered appearance. She had lost her hair to chemotherapy but had found the process character building. She knew and felt she was more, so much more, than the sum of her hair. As lovely as hair was, she was more proud of her attitude towards herself. She did have a wig which she loved but rarely wore, preferring to be free of any encumbrance. She was even happy to attend family outings and gatherings, not minding if photos were taken.

As it turned out, on occasion, this sometimes caused some confusion; especially when recollecting and reminiscing over family photos. This point was highlighted when her practically bald, seventy-something year old father quizzically looked at one particular snap and questioned why he was at that particular gathering. He couldn't understand why he had no recollection of the day at all, or why he would have even been there. Clare pointed out that the bald person in the picture was in fact herself, and teased him as to how he couldn't recognise his own daughter, feigning shock and disappointment.

She was in fact delighted, finding the whole situation highly amusing. It had often been commented on by family and friends just how much Clare resembled her father, clearly she had never realised how true this was.

Sadie

Running Away With You

Sadie had tried everything to keep from losing her hair during her cancer treatment, but to no avail. She had resigned herself to the inevitable and purchased a fabulous wig which made her feel a little better about the loss of her much loved tresses. When she spoke to her husband Al about the loss and what he thought she would look like having short or even no hair, he simply replied that Sadie had a pretty face and would resemble either an older Sinead O'Connor, or a young Judith Chalmers. A compliment indeed.

Sadie wasn't a person to dwell on the negatives in life. She was happy to chat and joke about the variety of indignities one went through when dealing with cancer, and she often regaled her listeners with her daily musings. The hair loss meant she became completely hair free.

Which she joked with her listeners resulted in no more waxing, shaving, or plucking; and as her energy levels had somewhat depleted that was fine by her. She hoped if she shared her thoughts and feelings with her BBC Essex Radio listeners, she would show and encourage others that there can still be life with cancer.

It was a cooler day at the beginning of Autumn, and Sadie had finished her radio show, and knew she needed to pop into her local Tesco to grab something for dinner that evening. She found she was a little more prone to forgetfulness since her treatments, and removing something from the freezer for meals was, more often than not, something she forgot.

As Sadie stepped over the supermarket threshold, she was greeted by the warm blast of air from within the supermarket. Sadie had an idea what she wanted and quickly headed to the aisles picking up a favourite main course and dessert. As she turned towards the checkout, Sadie was aware that her hands were wet, not just a little damp, but truly wet. After a second she felt what had caused the spectacle, her nose was running like a tap turned on full; not just a momentary drip, it was in full gush. Sadie had nothing to stop her nose, not tissue, nothing; not even her sleeve could stem the flow. Wearing a leather jacket meant she had nothing more than a very damp 'snail trail' as she tried desperately to shield her embarrassment.

By now she was at the checkout, thankfully there was no queue. 'I'm so sorry,' apologised Sadie, from behind her sleeve. 'I don't even have a tissue,' she laughed. The checkout lady grinned at Sadie, she knew who she was, and often listened to her radio show before starting her shift at the supermarket. She reached under the counter and located a packet of tissues. She popped them on top of Sadie's shopping, and then scooped all of the shopping into a carrier bag for the presenter. Smiling, she hooked the shopping bag onto Sadie's free hand, 'love your show'. She smiled as Sadie left the shop, her arm still across her face looking for all the world like a pantomime villain, all she needed was a black cape, only her eyes visible over her arm.

As soon as Sadie was free of the cosy interior, she felt the dripping ease and quickly located the tissues. Not having to shave your legs was great, but who knew there was a purpose for nasal hair. Sadie was roaring with laughter, barely coherent, as she regaled Al with the tale over dinner. She looked forward to sharing it again with her listeners the following morning.

Anon

Oooh! I Love Your Hairdo

For some reason, Jenny was a little embarrassed wearing her wig. She had undergone hours of debilitating treatment. Chemotherapy had robbed her of her hair, her eyebrows, and even leg hair, for which she was delighted; no more shaving.

For whatever reason though, she couldn't resign herself to wearing a wig. She felt she almost had to explain its presence, in an apologetic manner; as if to say 'sorry, you don't mind if my wig accompanies me today, do you?'

Jenny decided, if she wore it as often as possible she would begin to feel more comfortable about it. With this in mind, she wore the wig every time she stepped out of the house. This definitely seemed to help her feel more comfortable, but it was one particular trip to the supermarket that made her feel truly at peace with her hairpiece.

On a mundane trip with her daughter, while the food was being packed away at the checkout, Jenny noticed the cashier was an old friend, someone she had not seen for quite some time, but who had been part of a bigger circle of friends previous to her diagnosis and treatment.

'Hi Cath, how are you?', smiled Jenny. The woman looked up, and recognition spread across her face. 'Why Jenny, how are you? Gosh, it's been years since I saw you last.'

'I know! I'm good, thank you.' Jenny didn't feel the need to divulge her recent woes, she was happy to just indulge the need to chat.

'You look fabulous. Now that I know it's you I have to ask, where did you get your hair cut?' Cath was passing items through the scanner as she waited for Jenny to reply. Jenny paused for a moment before replying, 'It's a wig.'

'That's fantastic! What a great idea, wigs are all the rage at the moment. You can change your look without constant trips to the hairdresser.' Cath enthused.

Again, Jenny didn't feel the need to explain further. It was Cath that broke the pause in conversation. 'Can you give me the name of where you got it?' Cath then went on to briefly explain that she had just finished treatment for breast cancer, and although she enjoyed wearing a headscarf – something Jenny hadn't even noticed – she had now found the hairstyle she liked, Jenny's, and would love a wig just like it.

On the drive back home, Jenny realised upon reflection that she had become consumed with her own insecurities. She was not always completely aware of those around her, and by wearing her wig, she had actually proven inspirational to a friend who, as it turned out, had been on a similar cancer journey herself.

Jenny also began to realise that, if she looked at her wig as a fashion accessory no different to a bag, scarf, or jewellery, she could maybe even have some fun with it. Maybe, she mused, she would try a red shoulder length bob next, or even a brunette. The possibilities were endless.

Michelle
Drop Dead Gorgeous

Michelle had been through countless chemo-therapy treatments, and some of the treatments had been carried out at home. The nurses came to the house; often they were ladies, and the treatments would take anything from three to four hours.

Michelle was sitting at home, waiting patiently for her nurse to arrive when there was a knock at the door. Michelle opened the door to a 'wonderful surprise'; there stood a very hand-some young man. He had a leather jacket slung over his shoulder, and he was wearing Avia-tor sunglasses, looking for all the world like Tom Cruise in 'Top Gun'. The accompanying soundtrack was already in Michelle's mind as the song 'Take My Breath Away' broke into her thoughts. The young man cheerily asked for Michelle. Michelle replied eagerly 'That's me.' Sounding a little too enthusiastic for what was not a particularly pleasant procedure. 'My name's Rob, and I'm your chemo nurse.' He said, smiling.

With that, Michelle grabbed him and pulled him inside. He was so attentive, and drop dead gorgeous, that Michelle couldn't help herself; secretly texting her two single sisters, complete with surreptitious picture and a brief description of his attributes.

One of Michelle's sisters lived a good thirty minute drive away in another town, and the other one worked flexible hours and was at home, again a distance away. Within twenty five minutes of the text being sent, two cars could be heard screeching around the corner and coming to a skidding halt outside. Michelle watched as her sisters near sprinted up the garden path, in a race to get to the house first. Almost falling through the front door, the pair bundled into the house. One rushed to the bathroom, where Michelle could hear hairspray, deodorant, and perfume being liberally applied. The other wasted no time, and seized the opportunity to immediately ply the poor man with copious amounts of tea, coffee, biscuits, and anything else she could come up with.

Sister number one suddenly burst from the bathroom, looking like she was going on a night out, primped and preened to within an inch of her life, and surrounded by a cloud of hair product and perfume.

Michelle marvelled at the poor fella, he was so polite, and blushing. As he finished what he had come to do, he sat down on the sofa, a rookie mistake. In a flash, the two sisters had squeezed either side of him, and began firing countless questions as to his dating eligibility.

He took it all in good humour, and was very accommodating; Michelle guessed this wasn't the first time he had attracted such attention. What was normally a somewhat miserable day took on a distinctive cheerier note, and everyone left smiling.

Myer
Not Exactly Nicky Clarke

Myer had been an oncology nurse for the last ten years. During this time she had been involved with, and nursed people through, all aspects of cancer and oncology treatments. There was only one thing, one simple aspect she dreaded more than anything; helping people shave their heads. Although she dreaded it, she never refused, and sometimes it was where the most fun was had. One particular occasion, as she was called upon for her most dreaded task, was with a young man of about twenty who had suffered hair loss as soon as he started his chemotherapy treatment. He was studying to be a dentist, was 6'2" and weighed 100 kilos; not a small man by any means.

The young man's hair was a mass of thick curls and he needed it gone. But before it was removed completely he wanted to have some fun. Myer, as always, was a tad nervous. The young man asked if she could shave it first into a Mohawk style. Myer promised she would do her best, but couldn't guarantee the results. The patient took pictures throughout the process, with he and Myer laughing at all the weird stages his hair went through as it was being removed. Myer was the first to admit she was no Nicky Clarke, but between them, and the fits of laughter, the result was pretty impressive.

The young man sent pictures to his friends, and then, in a flash, he sent one last picture to his mother. With that done, the non-too-small and somewhat imposing young man quickly asked for the Mohawk to be shaved off completely, before his mum arrived and truly told him off! His friends were very impressed with his somewhat short lived hairstyle.

Lesley, Lynn & Don

Treatment Tag Team

Lesley was all set. Mel, her best friend, was pregnant in Dubai and was unable to fly home to Cambridgeshire when the news came through that both her parents had to undergo cancer treatments. Lynne was due to come home after her double mastectomy the same day Don had to be in hospital for a treatment for his own cancer. Lesley was Mel's closest friend, and her parents were like family, so there was no question as to who could help out at such a distressing time.

Mel's mum, Lynne, had been diagnosed with breast cancer, while Mel's dad, Don, was being treated for bowel cancer. What were the odds, that on the same date Lynne was due to be allowed home after her surgery Don would be undergoing a procedure himself?

The day arrived when Lesley was due to take care of both Lynne and Don; she had everything organised with military precision. With Mel in Dubai, Lesley had been keeping her constantly updated with her parents progress. Don had driven himself to Addenbrooke's for his treatment, assuring her he was more than capable of the drive.

Lesley had arrived at the huge hospital, and had quickly located both wards; as luck would have it they were at opposite ends of the vast hospital. Lesley was armed with gifts of chocolate for both her charges, a fine continental selection for Lynn and a multi-packet of Walnut Whips for Don, being at a loss as to what to buy him, and still questioning her dubious choice as she made her way through the corridors of the hospital.

Lesley had known Mel and her parents for years, and she was apprehensive as to how both would be after their respective procedures.

The hospital was hot, and she was already beginning to feel a little sweaty and flustered. She made her way to the ward where she knew Lynne had a room. The nurse showed her where Lynne's room was, and Lesley mentally prepared herself before entering. Popping her head around the door, she was greeted by the smiling, beautifully presented and impeccably made-up Lynne, looking as fabulous as ever, if a little stiff in her movements due to her dressings. Lesley was openly amused, and relief flooded through her. Lynne beamed at her, and gently patted the space beside her on the bed for Lesley to sit down.

"Darling, thank you so much for coming, this really is too much, you having to take care of us both like this." Lynne explained she was waiting to see the consultant, and then hoped to be discharged.

Lesley handed her the chocolates, and checked the clock on the wall. She had been chatting with Lynne for about an hour, and she knew she needed to get over to see how Don was. Lynne explained she was more than happy waiting for the consultant, and munching on her chocolates. Lesley was amazed at the picture of serenity her friend's mother was. Taking a deep breath, Lesley set off for Don's ward.

The maze of corridors seemed never ending, and Lesley could feel her feet beginning to ache, wishing she had been sensible enough to own a pair of trainers, never mind wear them. Wedges really weren't the footwear of choice for this type of trekking. She noticed her reflection in the large windows lining the corridors, and she could see she was already beginning to resemble someone who had undergone a strenuous session at the gym – something Lesley had never any inclination of doing – not someone visiting friends in hospital. She quickened her pace, and by the time she had reached Don's ward her hair was sticking to her head, resembling a blonde crash helmet. With Walnut Whips at the ready, and a quick pat down with her sleeve Lesley prepared to open the door to Don's room. She didn't know what to expect, and hoped she was prepared for anything.

Don was sitting on his bed, enjoying what looked like a fabulous Full English breakfast, beaming at her and professing to be enjoying every mouthful of his meal. Lesley was amazed, Don looked as bright and impeccably turned out as his wife. He too was waiting to be seen by his doctor, and then he hoped to be given the all-clear to go home. Lesley remembered she had Walnut Whips for Don and held out the now warm package. "Oooh! I haven't had these for years; I love them.' He beamed.

Lesley could feel her face reddening all the more, thanks to the combined efforts of physical exertion and the high temperature of the hospital. After sitting and chatting for a while, Lesley left Don and made her way back to Lynn. Bottled water purchased, she glugged down half its contents, stretched a little, smiling to herself as the theme tune to 'Chariots of Fire' played in her head, as she headed for the other ward. Physically panting, as Lesley reached for the handle of Lynne's room she tried desperately to smooth and style her now truly wayward hair and straighten her appearance a little.

'Darling, you look positively exhausted.' Professed Lynn, a concerned look on her face.

'No, no, I'm fine, honest.' Laughed Lesley, not admitting she was in fact completely exhausted, frazzled, and disastrously dishevelled. Lynne looking her usual fabulous self, only serving to accentuate Lesley's own bedraggled appearance. Lesley shared Lynne's delight at being told she could be discharged; just waiting for the correct paperwork so they would be able to leave.

Lesley, after catching her breath, set off once again to tell Don the good news; she surprised herself, quickly getting into her stride, and thought she might have even shaved a bit off her time as she let herself once more into Don's room. Don was delighted with the news about his wife, as was Lesley when he too confirmed he was almost ready to leave, and that he was also fine to drive himself home. After checking Don had everything ready, and arrangements made to meet him back at home, Lesley started on her way back to Lynne's room.

Doctors and nursing staff alike were now used to the sight of the blonde haired lady in the questionable footwear zipping along the busy corridors, nodding to her as she passed. 'Last time I think.' She called out to the orderly she had passed twice already throughout the day, and who had suggested she may actually want to consider getting a job at the hospital.

By the time Lesley reached Lynne her paperwork had been signed, and she already had everything packed away. Lesley slowly, and very carefully, escorted Lynne to her car and was grateful to at last be able to sit and take a very sedate drive home, sound in the knowledge that loved ones were well and back on the mend, as she gently massaged her calves before turning the key in the ignition.

Clare

On The Run

Clare had made a promise to herself; if she was well she would continue to run. She found running made her feel free and provided a great sense of well-being, as well as keeping her fit. Feeling the blood coursing through her, releasing the feel-good endorphins, and making her feel stronger and more capable of dealing with whatever life threw her way. When she was diagnosed with cancer, Clare knew so long as she was fit and strong enough; she would try and continue to run. During the treatments Clare ran as often as she was able, not always as far as she had in the past, but she viewed a run was a run, regardless of distance.

It was a good day, Clare was feeling well and looking forward to the run. With time to herself at last, she set out on the cold, bright morning. The air was crisp, and she felt it's chill against her skin. Breathing deeply and allowing the air to fill her lungs, she felt good, she felt alive.

Clare found the pounding of her feet against the pavement and uneven grassland therapeutic. Her heart felt lighter, and as she broke into her stride, the weight that seemed to nestle on her shoulders lifted. Coming around her last full circuit, she saw the lights of the local bakers cast a glow across the pavement in front of her. Quickly she ducked into the doorway, the bell over the door ringing as she stepped into the glowing interior. The warmth from within hit Clare in the face with a warm pow! In the very same moment Clare felt her nose twitch dramatically, and then with no warning, she felt a warm gush and was aware of a splashing sound on the tiled floor. It was a full minute before she saw there had been numerous splashes onto the tiled floor.

Clare realised the splashing had emanated from her. Simultaneously a handkerchief was handed to her by the lady behind the counter. 'I'm so sorry.' Clare laughed. As she quickly dabbed at her nose, she was engulfed in a mixture of embarrassment and unable to ignore the funny side of a full on gushing nose for all the world to see. She may well have lost her full head of hair, but she had not even comprehended nasal hair. She didn't even recall it being mentioned, but then she hadn't always fully listened to the dozens of possible side effects from her cancer treatment.

With a tissue held firmly to her nose, she collected the loaf she had ordered, tucked it under her arm, and headed back out into the cool air. Jogging back home Clare developed a stitch, she couldn't help but laugh at how she must have looked; laughing and jogging didn't really mix. Who knew nasal hair was so important?

Sadie

Love You, Mum

Sadie was someone who had seen a bit in her lifetime; having been involved in show business for decades, even having a recording career in the 1980's. All this meant she had come across a myriad of personalities. Sadie was more than capable of dealing with those who crossed her path; she liked to say she had "a look", a withering glare than sent many a combatant back from whence they came.

In dealing with her cancer, Sadie was equally defiant. She held the view that it was her cancer, and she would take it on any way she chose. This was Sadie's thinking from the offset. If she chose to deal with it with humour, however dark, that was how it was going to be, no questions asked.

Sadie was due for another bout of treatment, and whilst she was preparing for her second dose a nurse asked if it would be possible to tattoo two dots on her chest? This meant that whenever she came for subsequent treatments the dots would be aligned, and no further markings or adjustments would need to be made. The equipment could be aligned correctly on every occasion, and this would save an awful lot of time all round.

All this was explained in great detail to Sadie, who found the whole concept amusing, and her mind was already working mischievously. Sadie smiled, and then said 'You can do this of course, but can I have "I Love You Mum" tattooed instead?' The staff were momentarily speechless, and the room broke out into raucous laughter.

One nurse looked on disapprovingly, visibly tutting at the hilarity before her. Sadie caught the look on the nurse's face and flashed "the look", full beam, straight at her. Sadie and the nurse never crossed paths again, she did, however, have only the dots tattooed.

Anon

And The Award Goes To...

The boys had finally agreed to haircuts; having spent all summer looking like a cross between seven-year-old hippies or Old English Sheepdogs, with eyes close to being obscured by blonde wavy locks.

Nancy had asked her offspring to go and get haircuts. Haircuts were deemed a 'blue job' in her household. Having twin boys and one girl it was decided, with as near as possible democracy, with there being two females and three males, that there were now 'blue jobs' and 'pink jobs', especially as the children were growing up.

When Nancy had her cancer treatment explained to her she came very quickly to some decisions; her shoulder length, golden-streaked hair would have to go. She didn't think she could stand watching it fall out and, although there was no guarantee it would happen, she didn't want any further variable on top of dealing with the actual cancer.

Nancy had broached the subject with her family. Tabitha, being five, was easier to persuade a haircut was in order than the boys, Ben and Luke. It amazed Nancy how much her sons held on to her appearance. She wondered, if they perhaps saw no change, then there was nothing wrong; a sort of childlike 'head in the sand' approach. Nancy had been honest with her children about her illness, but in a very basic manner. They didn't need to know the specifics, but they did need to know mummy wasn't her normal self, and a few changes would need to be made.

Nancy's husband was a man who didn't care if his wife had long hair, short hair, or no hair at all. He had long ago shown that his love for his wife had little to do with her appearance. He had already joked with her about sporting a Sigourney Weaver from 'Aliens' look, and wasn't in the least bit surprised when Nancy told him that was exactly what she was going to do; she was going to have her hair shaved off in one go. The boys were outraged initially, but after Nancy and her husband had taped and stapled pictures from magazines of various film stars and celebrities sporting shorn looks they had finally calmed down.

What Nancy didn't tell them was that she intended to keep her hair in a little cloth pouch she had made for it. She planned a competition for the end of the summer holidays; as the boys hated having their own hair cut, she had allowed them to grow it over the summer, with the proviso they had good haircuts at the end of it.

At the same time as their haircuts, Nancy knew she would need to get her own done. Her treatment would have started, and she wanted her hair gone before it started to fall out on its own; she knew that would be far more distressing for all concerned than any haircut.

The haircut day came. Mike, Nancy's husband, was under strict instructions; short haircuts, but the hair from both boys was to be collected and put into ziplock bags and be brought home. Mike thought Nancy's idea was great. Nancy was having her hair shaved on the same morning, Tabitha was at her auntie's; Nancy felt this needed to be something done between her and her son's.

By lunchtime, everybody looked very different. Nancy was already home when she heard

Mike's car pull up. For the first time, Nancy felt slightly nervous. She was less shocked by her own appearance than she had thought she would be, and she hoped her children would feel the same. She had deliberately changed her look to try and make her new image whole. She was sporting jeans, a black sweatshirt, and lace up boots, looking more like a shorn Lara Croft than her usual 'country casual' style.

She heard the key in the lock. 'Ta-da' Nancy jumped out into the hallway as the three members of her family came through the front door, there was a stunned silence. Nancy felt her breath catch in her throat, a big smile on her face, and executing what she hoped was her 'cool mum' pose.

'Mum, you look fantastic!' Luke squealed

'Mum, you look so cool!' Ben laughed.

The relief Nancy felt almost made her burst into tears, and she stood for a moment, stemming the tears that were in danger of spilling onto her cheeks.

'That's not all,' she laughed 'We now have a competition too.' Nancy held both their hands and walked her sons into the lounge. Mike had the two bags of hair clippings, Nancy had hers.

'Drum roll please Daddy' said Nancy, as she took the three bags and told the boys there was a special prize for the person, or persons, whose hair clipping pile was the biggest. Nancy had already doctored her pile to be the smallest. The boys by this point had completely forgotten about their mother's change of appearance, and were concentrating on the competition. The drum roll was reaching a crescendo; the results were in. The tie between the boys was agreed with a great deal of whooping and dancing, and a prize of a new game for each of them was given. Nancy's hair was never long again, but it took a few more haircuts for Ben and Luke before they realised they were not going to get a new game every time they got their hair cut.

Susan
A Bit Like Grooming The Dog

Susan knew her hair was falling out. It was almost as if whenever she lifted her fingers to her head she came away with some hair in her hands.

Both she and her husband Casey had made sure their children were as accepting as possible of Susan's changing appearance, her general wellness and the fact that mummy wasn't well, as accepting as two young boys could be anyway. They wanted them to understand that everything mummy was going through was going to get her better. Wherever possible, the children were involved with little things to do with Susan's treatment and recovery. They were only small, the youngest barely a toddler, but they would help with tidying the toys away and sorting out clothes for school; little things that helped Susan and Casey when tiredness from the treatments took its toll.

Susan made the decision to get rid of what hair she had left. Her idea was to make sure that her children suffered minimal shock, and the way she thought that would be best achieved would be for them to be involved with the process. Coming up with a competition, Susan planned to get her children to race to see who could gather the most hair from mummy's head, using their hands, running them through her hair.

Susan did wonder what the boys would make of her idea, but thankfully they loved it. The competition was set, and there was a prize for the winner.

'On your marks, get set, go!' Announced their Dad, and with one son on each side of her Susan began to feel little hands rummaging through her hair. The boys loved the feel of the soft hair, and weren't in the least bit concerned as the soft tufts of hair filled their hands.

There were two small piles of hair, one on either side of Susan on the table which steadily grew. Soon the hair was pretty much gone from Susan's head. The warm hands on Susan's head felt almost natural, her children were having fun, doing an albeit unusual task. It was a task that needed to be done, one way or another, and what better way to make an event less shocking for two small boys than to get them involved? It saved on a visit to the hairdressers to boot!

The judging began, both boys had impressive piles of hair, and they were both clearly proud of their efforts. With backs turned to the competitors, both Mum and Dad conferred in whispered tones. There was a heavy pause; the children waited silently.

"The judges have decided to call the competition a draw." Casey pronounced in his most official voice. The whoops and cheers from the children and parents alike were loud and prolonged. Both boys were then given a prize, happy and very proud.

Anon

Olympic Hopes?

Mike had managed to keep his diagnosis quiet from his work and colleagues for some time. He felt well enough to work and had somehow managed to navigate his life around appointments, treatments, and symptoms. As his appearance wasn't affected too much, cancer often being a 'silent' illness, he carried on with life as normally as possible, feeling this was the approach that worked best for him in dealing with his cancer.

It was only when he started taking steroids as part of his treatment that his appearance changed dramatically. When his face began to swell, and he got the full measure of the 'moon face' side effects, he knew he could not keep his illness to himself any longer. Being a sales executive for an office furniture company, and constantly meeting clients and suppliers face-to-face, he was slightly concerned for his work. He had, in fact, no cause to be worried, and when the news was revealed there was nothing but full support from everyone, from the Managing Director down.

The head office for his employer was very near the Russian Embassy in London. There was a sales conference to attend by all sales staff, and Mike was looking forward to getting together, and seeing everyone he didn't often get to see in person. It was a great team building event too, and forged relationships no end. He knew there would be questions asked, but he was prepared and he was looking forward to the 'after conference' fun of socialising with some great friends and colleagues.

The conference was a busy affair, with lots of speakers, target projections, and new product lines showcased. Mike sat with other regional sales executives and happily joked about the steroid treatment, and how he could outperform any athlete in strength or speed, laughing that he would fail any drug test spectacularly.

At lunch time, a large group of the sales staff ventured out to take in a little of what central London had to offer. As the group passed the Russian Embassy, one of Mike's colleagues shouted across the group "Mike, quick, get yourself in there; you'll be signed up in a heartbeat for the next Olympics. You'll be a sensation, no questions asked.' The group fell about laughing. When Mike was able to stop laughing he agreed "Ah, yes, my Olympic dreams would come true after all.'

The group proceeded to take bets on Mike's chances in each organised event. It was agreed, with his steroid intake he could beat all comers, including the entire Russian team. Mike was an athletic superstar without even stepping foot on a track. An enthusiastic, and highly amusing lunch was taken by the group.

Del and Peter
Questioning Professor Hawking

Peter had been at sea from the age of fifteen; the ocean was his calling. After many decades of circumnavigating the globe, aboard everything from tankers to cruise liners, he and his family had settled in Essex, Mersea Island to be exact.

Peter married a beautiful South African nurse, and they had two children; they were all used to sunnier climes, and Mersea came as a bit of a shock. Although originally from Plaistow, Peter had loved everything about South Africa. The family had moved back to England in 1986, when he had the job of outfitting a cruise ship called the Astor from top to bottom.

It was only when he had been diagnosed with a very rare form of cancer, and had to undergo a dramatic and life changing operation – a radical amputation – that he slowed down. During his hospitalisation he had many visitors, one of his regulars being his nephew Del. Del was renowned for his mischevious antics, and had brought a smile more than once to his uncle's face throughout the cancer treatment and rehabilitation.

Peter was an avid reader, a highly intelligent man, and was working his way through two of Professor Stephen Hawking's books. On one occasion Del's visit coincided with a particularly down day for Peter; Del could see he was going to have to pull out all the stops to help his uncle. After messing around with the copious amounts of rubber gloves that were to hand in Peter's room, and to the exasperation of the nurses, Peter's mood had lifted a little.

When Peter was taken for therapy, Del found the two books on his uncle's bedside cabinet. Del knew his uncle would be some time, and had an idea for something to leave his uncle when he returned.

Del returned the following day; he could hear his uncle before he even saw him. Peter was sitting up in bed, voicing his outrage at what he was reading. Del was priviledged enough to be greeted by a barrage of expletives, as Peter explained how ridiculous he found Hawking's writing and findings. He was in the middle of ranting about how the world-renowned theoretical physicist couldn't write a book for toffee, and how he continually contradicted himself and continuity, and was frankly a fool.

It was as Peter saw his nephew's reaction, and the smile cross his face, that he realised something was afoot. "Go on, what did you do?" Del reached into the bedside cabinet. Realisation spread across Peter's face, "You swapped the books around didn't you?" There followed another tirade of unprintable words, the bookmark had been placed on the same page but in the second book. Del left his uncle's bedside that day, pleased with the fact that his uncle could still be heard laughing, albeit punctuated with the odd curse, as he made his way down the corridor to leave.

May The Force Be With You

Tana received the confirmation of her breast cancer via a phone call, while out collecting holiday money with her husband. It was a surreal moment with life buzzing around her, people shopping, talking on mobile phones. Life was carrying on and yet hers, in contrast, felt like it had ground to a halt; all time had stood still. Tana was a practical woman who was always mindful of those around her, especially loved ones.

The phone call had been taken as Tana was busy, and it was only when her and her husband were walking home that she broke the news to him in her usual stoic fashion. They walked and talked about all the possible outcomes of the conversation Tana had just had over the phone. Tana made light of the situation, and declared her boobs were a bit under the weather. She was adamant her condition would not be talked of in hushed tones, or only behind closed doors. Both her and her husband decided that names should be given for her boobs, making talking about them easier; she loved the fun aspect of the conversation. Her husband came up with a few that were not exactly what she had in mind. Eventually, they settled on Milly and Boo. Tana felt it would be easier to say she was having a problem with Milly or Boo. These then evolved into Mills and Boon; what could be easier than saying she was having a 'Mills and Boon' moment?

The hard part, as is often the case, was telling the rest of the family. They were a close family, despite living all over the world, and kept in contact regularly. Once the family was told, there was the decision to set up a WhatsApp group so they could all keep up to date with developments. What Tana wasn't aware of was there was a second group created, so the family were able to air their feelings or fears without Tana being aware of them. This meant that they gave their best positivity and good vibes to Tana, and kept any worries to themselves. Tana got nothing but the upbeat, positive, and healing conversations. The family could have their private meltdowns, but they were never shown or expressed to Tana; the WhatsApp groups worked perfectly. All were given 'Star Wars' character names, Tana being a massive Star Wars fan, and of course she was Princess Leia, abbreviated to PL.

After vast amounts of research, talking to others and asking countless questions, Tana decided to have surgery. The surgery went well, and her recovery was commented on as remarkable. As was her style, Tana found an upside to the major surgery she had undertaken; it came with a free tummy tuck! Bonus!

Irene

For The Camera

Irene had decided she would go and visit the local ladies support group, Brafternoon. She had been toying with the idea for a while and had decided today was the day. It took some courage, but she was sure when she got there and met other ladies, met the people she had heard so much about, she would be fine. Having had breast cancer, she wanted to connect with others, share in some of the positivity she had been told emanated from the group, its attendees, and organisers.

The hotel was beautiful, the day bright and sunny. Irene could hear the laughter and chatter as she approached the already open doors of the Garden Room where the group held their sessions.

With the sun streaming in, and the friendly vibe emanating from the room, Irene stepped inside. In a moment Irene was greeted with open arms and a sea of smiling faces, greetings were coming left and right. The room seemed to shine from within with happiness and positivity. Irene was asked to sign in, and was then shown to a table where there was tea, coffee, and biscuits; the place felt more like a ladies lunch party than a support group. Once Irene had got herself a drink she was introduced to a few of the other ladies, and then the organiser, Anita, asked if she wouldn't mind having a photograph taken for publicity purposes.

Irene was stumped for a moment. Pointing to her chest she replied 'What, a picture of these?' she smiled gesturing to her breasts. The roar of laughter was deafening. 'Your face, your face,' laughed the photographer rolling her eyes while trying to stop laughing as she focused the lens.

A great entrance to a great afternoon and a great day.

Val
I'm Forever Blowing Bubbles

Val had been ill with cancer for a long time, but today was a good day, and she was feeling better than she had in an age. She had decided she would make use of the Jacuzzi, and she had asked one of the nurses if they could get it ready for her. Yes, today would be a 'Pamper Val Day'. In no time, Val was called, her Jacuzzi was ready.

The room was softly lit, fragrant, and warm. Val already felt herself relaxing by just being in the room. Undressing, and Lowering herself into the water, she felt her body succumb to the beautiful warmth. A moment later, the jets turned on, and Val felt the gentle massage of the water against her skin. She sank lower into the heavenly water. The fragrance she had noticed when she came into the room seemed to be getting stronger, and felt as if it alone was easing away the tension in her body, it was a beautiful aroma of sandalwood and vanilla. Val closed her eyes and enjoyed the whole, relaxing sensation.

Val wasn't sure how long she had been enjoying her relaxation time when she noticed her nose becoming itchy. Yes, there was definitely something tickling it. Reluctantly, she opened her eyes; it took a moment to focus before the room came into clarity.

Val let out a gasp; she was up to her nose in bubbles. They were spilling over the top of the Jacuzzi and onto the floor. Everything was covered in a blanket of bubbles; she couldn't even see the floor tiles. Val knew she couldn't get herself out of the Jacuzzi without some assistance, and she had no idea, in the sea of bubbles, where the controls were to turn the jets off. Somebody must have put bubble bath into the Jacuzzi by accident.

Val couldn't help but chuckle, while she called out for someone to come and help her; there seemed to be no reply. She called again, as the room became more bubbles than anything else. She could barely make out the other bathroom fittings now, and the bubbles were steadily climbing the walls; tiny clouds were escaping in wisps into the air. The water jets kept on pumping. The water, or what was left of it was still warm, and Val wasn't uncomfortable, merely surrounded by vast clouds and cascades of bubbles.

She called as loudly as she could, realising there was going to be one enormous cleanup. She was sure she heard the door handle turn, but she could see no one through the sandalwood and vanilla scented fog.

In a moment, the gentle hum of the Jacuzzi stopped; there was silence. Like a scene from a movie, there were voices breaking through the bubble bank. 'Are you alright in there Val?' Val felt like she had a rescue party out on an expedition looking for her. Was she trapped on a mountain, scaling great heights, or deep in the jungle? No, she was lounging in a Jacuzzi. With this in mind, she chuckled again to herself.

Two hands, then a face full of concern came into view, still surrounded by the 'bubble mountain'.

'Val, we are so sorry. Someone must have thought you were having a bubble bath, not a Jacuzzi.' Val laughed out loud as she was helped out of the Jacuzzi by two nurses who now resembled fragrant snowmen. Wrapped in a warm towel, she was led out of the room as two other nurses passed her with wet and dry vacuum cleaners.

It took nearly twenty minutes to suck the room clean of bubbles. The Jacuzzi had to be rinsed countless times to ensure no more bubble escapades ensued in the future. The sucking sound of the two wet and dry vacuums could be heard for a long time after Val was made comfortable in her room, still laughing to herself.

Reports say the bathroom was sparkling, and the scent of sandalwood and vanilla hung in the air for weeks to come.

Wind, What wind?

Michelle had gone through so much treatment, and so many procedures, that she almost felt as though there was nothing else she could have.

Alas, further treatment was required, and Michelle, with renewed stoicism, accepted the decision. Unfortunately, her veins were not particularly compliant, and the medical staff were having a devils-own job of getting a vein to comply and accept the needle. After what seemed like a lifetime, it was decided there may be an accepting vein found in her arm, and the needle was to be placed there. Once the needle was finally placed, the nurse left the room.

Michelle sat with nothing but her own thoughts, while her treatment took place. Her arm began to swell. A million thoughts ran through Michelle's head as she tried to will the arm to stop swelling, wondering if this was what was supposed to happen? She had been told to alert anyone if she began to feel unwell, or noticed anything unusual. Not knowing if the swelling was unusual or not, and acknowledging she didn't feel any different, she was questioning herself constantly.

A nurse popped her head round the door. 'Are you ok?', 'Have you had wind?' Michelle was taken aback. 'No, I don't think so? Should I have? I don't feel gassy, should I burp? What should I do if I do? What does it mean if I have wind?' As Michelle worriedly fired the questions out she knew she was beginning to sound a little hysterical, but was genuinely concerned as to what she should and shouldn't be experiencing.

The nurse looked at her with a quizzical expression, one eyebrow raised. She paused for a moment and cleared her throat 'No, have you had Wyn, our little South African nurse tend to you at all?' The nurse pointedly replied, still looking sceptically at Michelle.

Michelle felt her whole body relax, and she burst out laughing. The nurse smiled at her, but it was obvious to Michelle the whole situation was far funnier to her than to the nurse, even after she was able to explain the joke.

Elsie and Cathleen

White As
A Ghost

Elsie and her younger roommate Cathleen had the same cancer, and were undergoing similar treatments. The ladies were laying in their respective beds, bemoaning as to their unkempt appearances. They had both wanted to have their hair washed, but they couldn't, and it was beginning to get them down.

Neither woman had any 'dry shampoo', which they were sure would help them feel better; a little more groomed if nothing else. One of the nurses had heard their complaints and had suggested talcum powder as an alternative. Initially, Cathleen and Elsie had laughed at the suggestion, but after a moment's contemplation Elsie decided she would give it a go.

Sitting on the edge of her bed, still laughing at the suggestion but desperate to make some improvement in her appearance, she carefully twisted the top of her talcum powder bottle. The pleasant aroma wafted up, and Elsie joked that if nothing else, her hair would smell nice.

Listening to the nurse's instructions, she had intended to lightly sprinkle the top of her head and then comb through the powder evenly. This, the nurse assured her, would leave her hair smelling fresh, looking clean, and easier to style; she would feel like a new woman. Cathleen watched her friend getting prepared, and she decided she would give it a go as well.

Unfortunately, what actually happened next was not quite what they expected. As soon as Elsie tipped the powder bottle upside down the top came off completely, and the entire contents was deposited on top of her head, shoulders and face. Without saying a word she turned to Cathleen, who was laughing uncontrollably, and unable to help in any way. Elsie was completely white, her eyes blinking through her ghost-like face. She couldn't help but laugh at herself, as the powder fell in great fragrant clouds around her with every movement. 'You look like a ghost.' Cathleen was finally able to say, her side aching from all the laughter. It was at that exact moment that the buzzer rang, indicating visiting time had just begun.

Both Elsie and Cathleen were still having fits of giggles, Elsie still white but beautifully fragrant as the first visitors of the day arrived.

Myer
Opposite Ends

Myer, through her experiences as an oncology nurse, found there were two subjects that were sometimes taboo. One was sex, and the other was poo.

These two topics often had folks divided. There were some patients, who often referred to themselves as 'frequent flyers', that had suffered more than one run-in with cancer. These were seasoned patients who had been there, seen it, done it, and got the T-shirt. They were happy to drop their underwear in a heartbeat to show off a newly healing radiotherapy site, or give a full and frank account of their findings with their latest stool sample, and how it came to be. As for sex, there would often be red faces all around as they divulged details of their sex lives. One man even commenting on just how unaffected his libido was, even though he was undergoing a gruelling chemotherapy regime, much to the utter embarrassment of his wife sat next to him.

The other end of the spectrum was often the newly diagnosed who, on top of being given sometimes devastating, certainly life changing news, then had to start revealing and recording the ins and outs of the most personal and private parts of their lives. Myer was always amazed how, in the end, everything was covered; the embarrassment was put aside, all matters were dealt with, even with a smile or two.

As a nurse, all cancers, treatments, and symptoms were approached with a caring and open mind, and always with an adaptability to the person's own mood. Throughout all her dealings, Myer always felt that her patients, be they young or old, were always looking for the next reason to laugh or make someone in the room smile. As a nurse, Myer felt it was her job to take her patients lead, and always walk into every unit, every day, with a smile for every patient.

Margaret

Hello Little Old Lady

Margaret was visiting her sons for the weekend. She loved spending time with her family and getting involved with their everyday lives. With her cancer treatments taking up so much time and effort it was good to be in the thick of normal family life, with its everyday ups and downs. Her chemotherapy had taken its toll, and she had lost all of her hair. She was sitting at the dressing table, trying to work out how to make herself feel and look vaguely human again, when her six-yead-old granddaughter came into the room and sat beside her.

Margaret had a scarf draped over her head, and her granddaughter Lola sat beside her, looking at her grandmother's reflection in the mirror; the two contemplated one another for a moment. Lola then cocked her head on one side and declared matter-of-factly, 'Oh, Nana, you look like a little old lady'. Margaret fell about laughing, thinking to herself, 'From the mouths of babes'. Lola was now laughing at her Nana, who was incapable of talking for laughing. Margaret marvelled at how children have the ability to be brutally honest, but never with malice; they simply tell it as they see it.

Margaret hugged her granddaughter tightly and began to wind the scarf around her head, still chuckling to herself.

Anon

Lizzie's Denial

Lizzie was a woman who had a tendency to put everyone else's feeling before her own. This was a commendable trait for sure, however, it had a habit of leading to denial on the part of Lizzie.

When Lizzie finally got herself to the doctor, after not feeling herself for some time, she was already on the way to playing down the feelings of fatigue, constant illness, and the unexplained swelling she had discovered as something to be ignored. She could well have sabotaged herself there and then, but her doctor knew Lizzie of old and sent her straight away for tests.

The tests came back showing abnormalities, again Lizzie played the whole matter down, her family behaved accordingly. Everyone went about their business as usual. When the date for her consultant's appointment arrived

Lizzie even attempted to go on her own, but her husband insisted on attending, and when the news was broken that Lizzie had cancer her response was typical. Even when she was taken into a separate consulting room to be alone with the Macmillan nurse, she insisted she was fine, and that was that.

Lizzie dismissed and trivialised as much as possible; this coming from her need to protect all those around her. It was only when her treatments began that Lizzie felt, perhaps, she was doing herself a disfavour.

There was one particular occasion, as she was suffering badly with sickness, her head firmly in the toilet bowl, with the much-loved family Labrador trying to lick her feet. She was also listening to her eldest daughter lament about lost loves, and latest boyfriend crushes, not pausing for breath other than to check that her mother was in fact still listening. Her husband was standing on the other side of the bathroom door, occasionally popping his head round to tell her what he had just discovered they had ran out of, grocery-wise, and Lizzie snapped. In between bouts of retching Lizzie firmly but politely told her daughter to buck up and shut up, gave the dog its marching orders and fished the Waitrose card out of her nearby handbag and promptly threw it in the direction of her husband, inadvertently bouncing it off her husband's head; she mumbled an apology and told him to 'go fill his boots' at the supermarket.

Within minutes the house was silent, and Lizzie was feeling a little better. Lizzie was no longer in denial, and she realised she felt so much better for it. Now it was time for a quiet cup of tea and to read a magazine.

Michelle

How's Your Ears?

Michelle had undergone a full hysterectomy, and was recovering in hospital. She was trying to get herself in as comfortable position as was possible under the circumstances, when a flustered consultant entered her room. He introduced himself; Michelle hadn't seen this particular consultant before, but during her treatments she had seen so many different people that it came as no surprise to meet someone new. With all the doctors and nurses coming and going in the busy ward, this was no surprise.

Bending toward Michelle, the consultant asked 'How are your ears?' Michelle was somewhat taken aback, wondering if there was a side effect that she was unaware of from the surgery. She had paid no attention to her hearing after the operation, so now that her attention was drawn to them she paused for a moment. No, her hearing was fine. 'And what about your nose?' The consultant asked. It was at this point that Michelle and her husband looked at each other questioningly. Again, Michelle's attention was drawn to her nose, a little runny maybe, but nothing untoward she decided.

The consultant then went on to examine her head area, moving her head from one side to the other, 'Well, this is very odd.' He muttered. Michelle began to panic slightly. The consultant then asked her to open her mouth, and he peered down her throat. Michelle heaved herself up straight as best she could, and opened her mouth as wide as possible. The consultant sounded exasperated and asked 'whatever is the matter with you?' Michelle explained that she was having difficulty moving due to the drains she had been fitted with after her Hysterectomy operation. "Op? Op? I'm the ear, nose, and throat specialist, not a gynaecologist. Who are you?' He asked, baffled and exasperated.

Needless to say, the consultant had gone into the wrong room, to see the wrong patient, about the wrong procedure. Michelle couldn't help but see the funny side of it all, and was pleased to know her ears were fine.

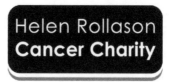

Helen Rollason
Cancer Charity

www.helenrollason.org.uk

Helen Rollason Cancer Charity is dedicated to supporting people whose lives are touched by cancer. Our support centres in Essex, London and Hertfordshire are vital in helping people living with cancer. The centres offer a range of complementary therapies to patients in an environment of peace and tranquillity, including counselling, reflexology, aromatherapy, manual lymphatic drainage and support groups. The centres are for patients with all types of cancer at all stages, whether newly diagnosed or longer term, throughout and after completion of treatment. Founded in 1999, the charity is the legacy of BBC broadcaster Helen Rollason, whose vision was:

"Good quality of life while coping with cancer is the most important gift a sick person can receive. It should be available to everyone."

Brafternoon

www.brafternoon.co.uk

Brafternoon is a not for profit group, whose sole aim is to provide a positive social experience, making a difference for ladies who have been affected by cancer.

With a wonderful setting and a great bunch of women, it has been succinctly said, that whilst 'having Cancer is a club that no one wants to be in'; 'Brafternoon is one club that everyone wants to be in!'

It offers a rare opportunity to spend time with ladies who really do understand; discussing a wide range of issues, swapping experiences and sharing activities - ultimately sharing one another's journey.

It's not all about Cancer; it's about giving women some 'me time' and an opportunity to leave everything else at the door for an afternoon.